NEW FOREST
PUB GUIDE

**CAMPAIGN
FOR
REAL ALE**

Published by the Southern Hampshire Branch of CAMRA

KEY *SYMBOLS*

DETAILS

Old Romsey Road, Cadnam, SO40 2NP
023 8081 2236   www.alcatraz.co.uk
SU291136   50.9211, -1.5871
1100-2300.

◖▶ S ✕ ⛺ ♿ ❀ ♨ P ☒

Ringwood: Best Bitter; one guest.
Westons: Scrumpy

Address
Telephone   Website
OS Grid Ref   Lat, Long
Opening Hours

Facilities (see below)
Real Ales
Real Ciders

FACILITIES

◖ **Lunchtime meals:** not snacks but substantial fare (including at least one hot dish).

▶ **Evening meals:** as for lunchtime meals.

S **Snacks:** snacks are served e.g. sandwiches; more substantial than a packet of crisps, but not a full meal.

✕ **Restaurant:** a separate restaurant, exclusively for those eating.

⛺ **Children welcome:** children are welcome in at least part of the establishment.

🐕 **Dogs welcome:** dogs are welcome in at least part of the establishment. Please telephone for clarification, if necessary.

♿ **Wheelchair access:** easy access to the pub and WCs. Many pubs without this symbol will assist disabled customers by arrangement.

🛏 **Accommodation:** rooms to let (no assessment of quality or price is made).

❀ **Outdoor drinking area:** this can vary from a garden to benches on a pavement, or even a village green.

♨ **Outdoor smoking area provided for drinkers:** a designated smoking area, sometimes heated and/or covered.

♨ **Real fire:** a fire fuelled by coal or wood.

Å **Camping:** camping and/or caravanning facilities at the pub or within ½ mile. Description may note camping beyond this distance.

P **Pub has its own car park**

⇌ **Railway station:** there is a railway station within ½ mile. See also the public transport section of this guide for further details.

☒ **Near bus stop:** there is a bus stop within ½ mile. See also the public transport section of this guide for further details.

CONTENTS

Acknowledgements

Producing this guide would not have be possible without the unpaid volunteers who gave their time to coordinate, survey, describe, photograph and proof-read. The *CAMRA New Forest Pub Guide* Editorial Team thanks:

Jim Andrews; Terry Ashmore; Tim Bacon; Andrew Burrows; Mike Chilcott; Terry Cowling: Drew Dyer; Steve Eatwell; David Etheridge; Alan Ford; Graeme Hilton; Zena Hilton; Alan Judd; Graham Kesby; John Lambert; Guy Lawrenson; Karen Magill; Shaun Magill; Ray Massey; Sue Massey; Ash Mather; Jon Nicholas; Danny O'Connell; Pat O'Neill; Deric Payne; Alex Presland; David Pritchard; Mich Rice; Dave Richardson; Phillip Scott-Kilner; Nick Thorne; Barry Wharton; Rob Whatley.

Cover photograph: PhotoNewForest.com 01590 681544
Design and typesetting: John Buckley, jpbdesign.net 01256 892650
Outline map: Creativelyso.co.uk 07872 554141

Parishes with no pubs
Readers with detailed knowledge of the guide area and an attention to detail will have noticed some missing parishes. There are six parishes or part-parishes that do not have any pubs, these are: Exbury and Lepe; Hale; Martin; Melchet Park and Plaitford; Sandleheath; Whiteparish.

INTRODUCTION

GENESIS

CAMRA's Hampshire branches last published a guide to the county's pubs in 1994. For years members of Southern Hampshire branch desired an up-to-date guide to pubs in its area, until deciding to produce a guide to the New Forest (National Park and District). A committee was formed, and a task force was dispatched to observe, question and report.

The result is this book.

GUIDE ORGANIZATION

Pubs are listed within settlements grouped within the well-defined boundaries of civil parishes.

THE ENTRIES

The criterion for an establishment's inclusion in this guide, other than that of location, is that a non-resident, non-diner can purchase and consume alcohol on the premises. Real ales and real ciders served are listed, but availability is not a criterion for inclusion; absence today does not imply absence tomorrow.

THE NEW FOREST

The National Park contains the largest area of lowland heath in Europe, tracts of bog, dense woodland, broad lawns, farmland, and unspoilt coastline. The District adds the rolling hills of the western borderland, and the populous areas of Waterside and Totton.

The ubiquitous ponies are not wild, they are are owned by commoners, as are the cattle, donkeys, pigs and sheep. The Forest is also home to five species of deer and an abundance of smaller creatures.

Places of interest are included in pub descriptions, but we do not claim comprehensiveness; much remains for you to discover.

OUT AND ABOUT

To assist your exploration we have included maps and basic public transport information. For cyclists and walkers we recommend the Ordnance Survey's 1:25,000 map of the New Forest. To all we recommend the Visitor Information Centres in Lyndhurst and Lymington.

UPDATES AND CORRECTIONS

Errors occur; things change – please tell us of any significant changes through our website, where new and revised information will be published:

www.shantscamra.org.uk/beer/newforest/

SATELLITE NAVIGATION

For digital assistance in locating pubs, you may download Point of Interest files for compatible TomTom, Garmin and Navman devices from our website:

www.shantscamra.org.uk/beer/newforest/

AN INSUBSTANTIAL HISTORY OF THE NEW FOREST

WHAT'S IN A NAME?

It is not new, and much of it is not forest.

The New Forest was created by William I (the Conqueror) in 1079. The designation forest signified the applicability of forest law, whereby the king enjoyed rights to a forest's natural resources, and the common folk enjoyed mutilation for endeavouring to experience similar pleasures. Vestiges of forest law remained until 1971.

NEW FOREST NATIONAL PARK

The New Forest National Park was created in March 2005.

A FAMOUS DEATH

On 2 August 1100, William's son, William II, whose ruddy complexion earned him the nickname Rufus, was killed during a hunting trip, perhaps accidentally, perhaps by Sir Walter Tyrrell's arrow, and perhaps at the site marked by the Rufus Stone.

THE OLD ENEMY

In the 16th century, Henry VIII's castles at Calshot and Hurst were built as defences against a French or Spanish invasion. From the 1700s until the advent of the ironclad, many warships, including vessels for Nelson's navy, were built at Bucklers Hard.

THE WORLD WARS

Buildings were commandeered by the military, camps were built for servicemen, land was converted to farming use, and Forest timber fed the war effort.

Lepe was a D-day departure point; parts of the Mulberry Harbours were built nearby, and PLUTO (Pipeline Under The Ocean) stretched from Lepe to France to deliver fuel to the invasion force. Barnes Wallis's bouncing bomb was tested at Ashley Range (near Godshill), and warplanes flew from the Forest's many airfields.

Calshot was home to seaplanes and flying-boats. After the 2nd World War was over, two of the ill-fated, giant Princess flying boats stood near the hangars – silent, cocooned and awaiting the scrapyard.

INDUSTRY

The major industries now are oil-refining, forestry and tourism. The saltworks at Lymington closed more than a century ago, and gunpowder is no longer manufactured near Fritham.

NEW FOREST SHOW

The New Forest Show takes place at New Park, Brockenhurst in late July, and provides local education, entertainment and refreshment to thousands.

THE BREWING PROCESS

HOW IS BEER MADE?

THE BREWING PROCESS is essentially cooking on an industrial scale. There are just four raw materials: water, malt, hops and yeast. The water, softer for mild beers harder for bitters, is always known, curiously, to the brewer as his liquor. Malt is made from barley; the grain is allowed to grow for a day or so to develop enzymes that turn the starchy grain into sugars that would feed the plant but the maltster arrests this by heating and drying the kernels. Hops, which supply both flavour and aroma, are the dried flowers of a vigorous climbing plant, and the yeast is a single-celled fungus.

At the start of his day the brewer takes sacks of malt and mills them into a rough flour which is run into a huge saucepan (the mash tun) and steeped in hot liquor (water) to make a porridge-like mass. Within this porridge the enzymes in the malt convert the starch into a variety of sugar compounds which dissolve in the liquid. After an hour or so the liquid (now called wort) is run off into a huge kettle. The hops are added and the mixture is boiled vigorously. The liquid (now called hopped wort) is run off through a cooler into the fermentation vessels. Some yeast is added to each vessel and they are left for about a week.

During that week the yeast multiplies, feeds on the sugars and excretes alcohol as its waste product; the result is beer. Excess yeast is skimmed off (going to the food industry to make yeast extracts) and the beer is run off into a maturing tank. After another week or two it is racked into the casks for delivery to the pub. As the beer is put into the casks some finings are added; over time this slimy material, resembling egg white, coagulates the residual yeast leaving the beer clear to serve. Although the finings clear the beer the residual yeast is still sufficiently active to produce CO_2 to keep the beer sprightly.

REAL ALE *STYLES*

REAL ALE IS A NATURAL PRODUCT brewed using traditional ingredients and left to mature in the cask delivered to the pub, through a process called secondary fermentation. It is this process which makes real ale unique amongst beers and develops the wonderful tastes and aromas which processed beers can never provide.

The capacity of a brewery is measured as the volume, in barrels (36 gallons), in a single brew – typically only one brew can be started per day.

Real Ale comes in a variety of styles, listed below, but every beer has its own unique flavour, aroma, strength and colour. The best way of appreciating the various styles of beer is simply to try them!

BITTER
Bitter is the most common beer style. Typically straw to copper in colour, with a hop fragrance and bitter finish, although many can be fruity and/or malty. Stronger bitters are often called Best Bitter.

MILD
A traditional style of beer that was originally more popular than Bitter. Normally dark brown in colour, due to the use of well-roasted malts, but paler versions do exist. Typically it has rich malty aromas and flavours, with only a slight hint of hops.

OLD ALE
Rich in flavour and high in strength, old ales are typically aged in the cask for several weeks.

PORTER
Typically black, due to dark malt used in production, with a rich, fruity taste and well marked bitterness.

STOUT
Similar to Porter, but with a sweeter and less bitter flavour.

BARLEY WINE
Typically very strong in flavour, as well as in strength. Often with intense fruit flavours and having any colour from light brown to black.

INDIA PALE ALE (IPA)
Golden coloured ale originally brewed in the 19th century for the colonial market. Its high strength and large amount of hops allowed the ale to survive the long voyages. The name is widely used by brewers for many ordinary bitters.

PALE ALE
A derivative of IPA that is weaker and less hoppy, typically having a spicy aroma with biscuit malt and citrus fruit flavour.

GOLDEN ALE
A recent and very popular style of beer, similar to Pale Ale but with a modern twist – typically using paler malts and a variety of hops. They have a variety of flavours and aromas, such as citrus and floral, normally with a crisp, quenching finish.

BREWERIES& *BEERS*

Seasonal and special beers are omitted from this list.

NEW FOREST

These breweries and a cider maker lie within this guide's boundary.

Red Shoot Brewery (Wadworth), Linwood, Hampshire
2½ barrel brewery in a Wadworth pub. Commissioned in 1998.
① 01425 475792   www.redshoot.co.uk
New Forest Gold (3.8%) *Bitter*   Tom's Tipple (4.8%) *Bitter*
Muddy Boot (4.2%) *Mild*

Ringwood Brewery (Marston's), Ringwood, Hampshire
Bought in 2007 by Marston's; plans to increase to 50,000 barrels a year.
① 01425 471177   www.ringwoodbrewery.co.uk
Best Bitter (3.8%) *Bitter*   Fortyniner (4.9%) *Bitter*
Old Thumper (5.6%) *Bitter*

New Forest Cider, Burley, Hampshire
Producer of Snake Catcher cider, using apples including those grown on its farm.
① 01425 403589   www.newforestcider.co.uk
Sweet *Cider*   Dry *Cider*
Medium *Cider*   Kingston Black *Cider*

LOCALE

CAMRA's LocAle scheme promotes local beers for local
pubs. These breweries lie within 25 miles of the boundary of this guide.

Botley Brewery, Botley, Hampshire
Cider producer, using apples grown on its farm and local orchards.
① 01489 784867   www.botleybrewery.co.uk
5-barrel brewery that began production in 2010.
Botley Mill (3.8%) *Bitter*   Gringo's Gold (4.5%) *Golden ale*
Botta's Best (4.2%) *Bitter*   Old Cooperage (5.0%) *IPA*

Bowman Ales, Droxford, Hampshire
20-barrel brewery established in 2006 in converted farm buildings.
① 01489 878110   www.bowman-ales.com
Elderado (3.5%) *Golden ale*   Wallops Wood (4.0%) *Bitter*
Swift One (3.8%) *Golden ale*   Quiver (4.5%) *Golden ale*

Downton Brewery, Downton, Wiltshire
20-barrel brewery established 2003; equipment leased from Hop Back.
① 01725 513313   www.downtonbrewery.com
New Forest Ale (3.8%) *Bitter*   Honey Blonde (4.3%) *Golden ale*
Quadhop (3.9%) *Golden ale*   Dark Delight (5.5%) *Old ale*
Elderquad (4.0%) *Pale ale*

Flack Manor Brewery, Romsey, Hampshire
20-barrel brewery that commenced operation in 2010.
① 01794 518520   www.flackmanor.co.uk
Double Drop (3.7%) *Bitter*   Flack Catcher (4.4%) *Bitter*

Flowerpots Brewery, Cheriton, Hampshire
Next to the Flowerpots Inn; brewing commenced in 2006.
① 01962 771534   www.flowerpots-inn.co.uk
Perridge Pale (3.6%) *Pale ale*   Goodens Gold (4.8%) *Bitter*
Flowerpots Bitter (3.8%) *Bitter*   Flowerpots IPA (6.0%) *IPA*
Cheriton Porter (4.2%) *Porter*

Goddards Brewery, Ryde, Isle of Wight
Established in 1993 in an 18th century barn and relocated in 2008.
① 01983 611011   www.goddardsbrewery.com
Ale of Wight (3.7%) *Pale ale*   Fuggle-Dee-Dum (4.8%) *Bitter*
Scrumdiggity (4.0%) *Bitter*

Gribble Brewery, Oving, West Sussex
Established by Hall & Woodhouse; independent since 2005.
① 01243 786893   www.gribbleinn.co.uk
Gribble Ale (4.1%) *Bitter*   Plucking Pheasant (5.2%) *Bitter*
Reg's Tipple (5.0%) *Old ale*

Hall & Woodhouse (Badger), Blandford St Mary, Dorset
A large, independent family brewer founded in 1777.
① 01258 452141   www.hall-woodhouse.co.uk
K&B Sussex (3.5%) *Bitter*   Tanglefoot (4.9%) *Bitter*
Badger First Gold (4.0%) *Bitter*

Havant Brewery, Cowplain, Hampshire
Began brewing in 2009 as a one barrel plant.
① 023 9225 2118   www.thehavantbrewery.co.uk
Started (4.0%) *Bitter*   Finished (5.0%) *Old ale*
Stopped Dancing (4.4%) *Golden ale*

Hensting Brewery, Owslebury, Hampshire
Established in 2010, using barley grown on the owner's farm.
① 07775 601827   www.henstingbrewery.co.uk
Winchester Gallon (4.4%) *Golden ale*

Hop Back Brewery, Downton, Wiltshire
Founded in 1987 at a Salisbury pub; now relocated and expanded.
① 01725 510986   www.hopback.co.uk
GFB (3.5%) *Bitter*   Taiphoon (4.2%) *Golden ale*
Odyssey (4.0%) *Bitter*   Entire Stout (4.5%) *Stout*
Crop Circle (4.2%) *Golden ale*   Summer Lightning (5.0%) *Golden ale*

Irving & Co Brewers, Portsmouth, Hampshire
① 023 9238 9988   www.irvingbrewers.co.uk
Set up by a former Gale's brewer using a 15 barrel plant.
Frigate (3.8%) *Bitter*   Invincible (4.6%) *Bitter*
Type 42 (4.2%) *Bitter*

Isle of Purbeck Brewery, Studland, Dorset
10-barrel plant on the Jurassic Coast, founded in 2002.
① 01929 450227   www.isleofpurbeckbrewery.com
Best Bitter (3.6%) *Bitter*   Studland Bay Wrecked (4.5%) *Bitter*
Fossil Fuel (4.1%) *Bitter*   Purbeck IPA (4.8%) *IPA*
Solar Power (4.3%) *Golden ale*

Itchen Valley Brewery, New Alresford, Hampshire
Established in 1997 and moved to new premises in 2006.
① 01962 735111   www.itchenvalley.com
Godfathers (3.8%) *Bitter*   Winchester Ale (4.5%) *Bitter*
Fagin's (4.1%) *Bitter*   Pure Gold (4.8%) *Golden ale*
Hampshire Rose (4.2%) *Golden ale*

Keystone Brewery, Berwick St Leonard, Wiltshire
10-barrel plant founded 2006. The brewery espouses sustainability.
① 01747 820426   www.keystonebrewery.co.uk
Bedrock (3.6%) *Golden ale*   Large One (4.2%) *Bitter*
Gold Spice (4.0%) *Golden ale*   Very Pale Ale (4.6%) *Pale ale*
Gold Standard (4.0%) *Golden ale*   Cornerstone (4.8%) *Old ale*

Oakleaf Brewery, Gosport, Hampshire
Brewery on the side of Portsmouth Harbour, established in 2000.
① 023 9251 3222
Some Are Drinking (3.9%) *Bitter*
Quercus Folium (4.0%) *Bitter*
Nuptu'ale (4.2%) *Pale ale*
Pompey Royal (4.5%) *Bitter*
Hole Hearted (4.7%) *Bitter*
Blake's Gosport Bitter (5.2%) *Old Ale*

www.oakleafbrewing.co.uk
For Suthwyk Ales:
Old Dick (3.8%) *Bitter*
Liberation (4.2%) *Golden ale*
Skew Sunshine Ale (4.6%) *Golden ale*
Palmerston's Folly (4.8%) *Pale ale*

Plain Ales Brewery, Sutton Veny, Wiltshire
Started in 2008 as a 2½ barrel plant, now expanded to 10 barrels.
① 01985 841481
Innocence (4.0%) *Golden ale*
Innspiration (4.0%) *Bitter*

www.plainales.co.uk
Inndulgence (4.5%) *Porter*

Small Paul's Brewery, Gillingham, Dorset
Launched in 2006 by a home brewer using a ½ barrel plant.
① 01747 823574
Gylla's Gold (3.8%) *Golden ale*
Wyvern (4.4%) *Bitter*

Gillingham Pale (4.5%) *Pale ale*

Stonehenge Ales, Netheravon, Wiltshire
Created in 1984 as Bunce's in an old mill; the new owner renamed it in 1994.
① 01980 670631
Spire Ale (3.8%) *Bitter*
Pigswill (4.0%) *Bitter*
Heelstone (4.3%) *Bitter*

www.stonehengeales.co.uk
Great Bustard (4.8%) *Bitter*
Danish Dynamite (5.0%) *Golden ale*

Three Castles Brewery, Pewsey, Wiltshire
An independent, family-run brewery established in 2006.
① 01672 564433
Barbury Castle (3.9%) *Pale ale*
Uffington Castle (4.2%) *Old ale*

www.threecastlesbrewery.co.uk
Vale Ale (4.3%) *Golden ale*
Tanked Up (5.0%) *Old ale*

Triple fff Brewery, Four Marks, Hampshire
A 50 barrel brewery founded in 1997 with a 5 barrel plant.
① 01420 561422
Alton's Pride (3.8%) *Bitter*
Pressed Rat & Warthog (3.8%) *Mild*

www.triplefff.com
Moondance (4.2%) *Bitter*

Upham Brewery, Upham, Hampshire
Upham began brewing in 2009 using a 3½ barrel plant.
① 01489 861383
Upham Ale (4.0%) *Bitter*

www.uphambrewery.co.uk
Stakes Ale (4.6%) *Bitter*

Wessex Brewery, Longbridge Deverill, Wiltshire
Started in 2001 and moved to its current location in 2004.
① 01985 844532
Potter's Ale (3.8%) *Bitter*
Longleat Pride (4.0%) *Bitter*
Crockerton Classic (4.1%) *Bitter*
Merrie Mink (4.2%) *Bitter*

Deverill's Advocate (4.5%) *Golden ale*
Warminster Warrior (4.5%) *Bitter*
Russian Stoat (9.0%) *Stout*

Yates Brewery, Newchurch, Isle of Wight
Established in 2000 in St Lawrence; now a 10 barrel plant in Newchurch.
① 01983 867878
Best Bitter (3.8%) *Bitter*
Undercliff Experience (4.1%) *Bitter*
Blonde Ale (4.5%) *Golden ale*

www.yates-brewery.co.uk
Holy Joe (4.9%) *Golden ale*
White Winter (5.0%) *Old ale*
Special Draught (5.5%) *Old ale*

RINGWOOD *BREWERY*

BEER AND RINGWOOD go hand in hand as brewing has been part of the town's heritage for centuries. Today Ringwood Brewery is the custodian of this heritage and has been crafting quality beers such as our much loved Best Bitter, Fortyniner, Boondoggle and the revered Old Thumper. Did you know…Old Thumper was voted Champion Beer of Britain in 1988 by CAMRA.

Our award winning beers are brewed in the traditional way using only the finest natural ingredients, premium malted barley from Hampshire, Dorset and Devon together with hops from the best growers in Kent and Worcestershire. The rest is down to our famous yeast strain and the skill and dedication of our brewers.

BREWERY VISITS

Why not book yourself onto our Brewery Tour experience where you will get the opportunity to partake in a tutored tasting session and enjoy a complimentary drink in the Pin Room.

Booking a Brewery Tour is easy…
call 01425 470303
or visit
www.ringwoodbrewery.co.uk

PUBLIC *TRANSPORT*

The Hythe Ferry Train

THE PAST IS A FOREIGN COUNTRY

The rail lines between Ringwood and Brockenhurst, and between Salisbury and West Moors (serving Fordingbridge and Breamore) closed in 1964; the Totton to Fawley branch saw its last scheduled passenger train in 1966.

Never again shall we catch the bus to Emery Down and Robin's Bush, or ride the 39 on Deadman Hill and Godshill Ridge. The bus to the Royal Oak at Fritham made its last depot run long ago, and few would now believe that buses used to turn at Stoney Cross.

A BRIEF INTRODUCTION TO THE PRESENT

The main centres of population are still well-served by public transport, although there may be few buses on Sundays and in the evenings. Provided one is willing to walk a little way, it is still possible to visit the vast majority of the hostelries in this guide without recourse to a car.

RAIL SERVICES ⇌

The London Waterloo – Weymouth main line bisects the New Forest on its route between Southampton and Bournemouth; a branch line to Lymington leaves the main line at Brockenhurst. Services through and within the Forest are operated by CrossCountry and South West Trains.

Times

Free timetable booklets are available from all staffed stations. South West Trains also publishes a book containing details of all of its services; this is available from major stations and by mail order. Timetables showing all rail services in Great Britain are published by TSO and by Middleton Press; these are available by mail order and at some station bookstores.

Information may also be found on the following websites:

National Rail	www.nationalrail.co.uk
CrossCountry	www.crosscountrytrains.co.uk
South West Trains	www.southwesttrains.co.uk

BUS SERVICES

Most services are operated by Bluestar or Wilts & Dorset, but infrequent services to remote or less populous villages may be provided by smaller operators.

Times

Bluestar publishes a comprehensive timetable booklet; Wilts & Dorset publishes various booklets and leaflets; these are available from the operators and from Tourist Information Centres. Printed information about other operators' services can be hard to find. Information may also be found on the following websites:

Bluestar	www.bluestarbus.co.uk
Wilts & Dorset:	www.wdbus.co.uk
Traveline South West	www.travelinesw.com

Tickets for Unlimited Travel

Bluestar and Wilts & Dorset sell a range of tickets permitting unlimited travel in specified areas within their networks, and an Explorer ticket which permits unlimited travel throughout their combined network and beyond.

FERRY SERVICES ⛴

White Horse Ferries operates a passenger service between Hythe and Southampton. Wightlink operates a passenger and vehicle service between Lymington and Yarmouth. Ferries also operate from Keyhaven to Hurst Castle (when the castle is open) and Yarmouth (during summer).

Times

Leaflets are available from operators and Tourist Information Centres; information may also be found on the following websites:

White Horse Ferries	www.hytheferry.co.uk
Wightlink	www.wightlink.co.uk
Hurst Castle	www.hurstcastle.co.uk

Service Index

The table lists every settlement for which there is an entry in the guide, its rail station and ferry services, and either the route numbers of buses serving that settlement (excluding school buses) or the name of and distance to the nearest settlement served by bus.

Notes

1. This table does not distinguish between a frequent daily service and a once a week service. Refer to timetables if you want to be neither disappointed nor stranded.
2. NFT is the summer only New Forest Tour bus.

Settlement	Service
Ashford	*See Fordingbridge (½ mile)*
Ashley	192 194 195 X2
Ashurst	⇌ Ashurst (New Forest)
	6
Avon	175
Bank	*See Lyndhurst (1¼ miles)*
Bartley	10 11
Barton on Sea	194 195 X1
Battramsley	6 NFT
Beaulieu	112 NFT
Beaulieu Road	⇌ Beaulieu Road
	NFT
Blackfield	9 H3
Boldre	6 112
Bowling Green	C32 C33 X2
Bramshaw	*See Nomansland (2 miles)*
Bransgore	175 176
Breamore	49 X3
Brockenhurst	⇌ Brockenhurst
	6 NFT
Brook	*See Cadnam (1½ miles)*
Bucklers Hard	*See Beaulieu (2¼ miles)*
Burgate	X3
Burley	176
Cadnam	10 11
Calmore	11 12
Calshot	9 H3
Canada	39 X7 X71
Canterton	*See Cadnam (2 miles)*
Copythorne	11
Damerham	301 302
Dibden	8
Dibden Purlieu	8 9 H1 H2
Downton	X1
East Boldre	112
East End	112
Eling	8 9
Emery Down	*See Lyndhurst (1 mile)*
Everton	118 X1
Fawley	9 H3
Fordingbridge	49 X3
Fritham	*See Nomansland (3¼ miles)*
Frogham	*See Fordingbridge (2 miles)*
Godshill	*See Fordingbridge (2 miles)*
Hamptworth	39 X7 X71
Hardley	9 H3
Hill Top	112
Hinton Admiral	⇌ Hinton Admiral
	118 X1 X2
Hinton St Michael	*See Hinton Admiral (1½ miles)*
Holbury	9 H3
Hordle	118 192 X2
Hounsdown	8 9
Hythe	⛴ Southampton
	8 9 H1 H2 H3 112
Ibsley	X3
Keyhaven	⛴ Hurst Castle
	⛴ Yarmouth
	See Milford-on-Sea (1 mile)
Landford	X7 X71
Langley	9
Linwood	*See Ibsley (3¾ miles)*
Lymington	⇌ Lymington Town
	6 112 118 119 C32 C33 X1
	X2 NFT
Lyndhurst	6 NFT
Marchwood	8 9
Milford on Sea	X1
Minstead	*See Cadnam (2¼ miles)*
Mount Pleasant	*See Bowling Green (1 mile)*
Netley Marsh	10 11
New Milton	⇌ New Milton
	118 191 192 194 195 C32
	C33 X1 X2
Nomansland	39 X7 X71
North Gorley	X3
Ower	X7 X71
Pennington	119 X2
Pilley	112
Poulner	136 137
Redlynch	44
Ringwood	36 36A 38 118 136 137 175
	176 303 X3 X55
Rockbourne	*See Damerham (2 miles)*
Rockford	*See Ibsley (1¼ miles)*
Setley	6 NFT
Sopley	175
Stuckton	*See Fordingbridge (¾ mile)*
Sway	C32 C33
Tiptoe	C32 C33
Totton	⇌ Totton
	8 10 11 12 T1 T2 6 X7 X71
Walhampton	⇌ Lymington Pier
	⛴ Yarmouth
	See Lymington (1 mile)
Whitsbury	49
Winsor	11
Woodgreen	*See Breamore (1 mile)*
Wootton	C32 C33

ASHURST
FOREST INN

MAP E (5)

⌖ Lyndhurst Road, Ashurst, SO40 7DU
☎ 023 8029 3071
↗ SU343108   50.8960, -1.5136
🕐 1130-2330 Mo-Sa; 1200-2300 Su.

◖▶ S ✗ ⛺ 🐕 ❀ ♨ P ⇌ 🚌

🍺 Ringwood: Best Bitter, Fortyniner; two guests.

"He was a wise man who
invented beer."
PLATO

This chalet-style pub lies back from the road and can easily be missed; it was recently renovated following a period of closure. The interior is divided in two by a large, brick fireplace; the restaurant is to one side, in a raised area, and to the other side is the bar area, with comfortable chairs before the fire. Food is served all day Saturday and Sunday. Dogs are welcome only in the bar area.

ASHURST
HAPPY CHEESE

MAP D (6)

⌖ 189 Lyndhurst Road, Ashurst, SO40 7AR
☎ 023 8029 3929   www.thehappycheese.co.uk
↗ SU336103   50.8920, -1.5232
🕐 1100-2300.

◖▶ S ⛺ 🐕 ♿ ❀ ♨ ⌁ 🅰 P ⇌ 🚌

🍺 Flack Manor: Double Drop; Ringwood: Best Bitter, Fortyniner.

This single storey pub is decorated in rustic style. Food is sourced locally: meat and eggs come from nearby Longdown Activity Farm, cheese from Lyburn dairy. Special dietary requirements are catered for, and takeaways can be provided for prospective fathers waiting at the nearby maternity hospital. Food is served all day. When Ashurst campsite is busy the pub opens at 10am for breakfasts. There is a bouncy castle in the garden during summer. A beer festival is held during the August bank holiday weekend.

BEAULIEU
MONTAGU ARMS HOTEL

MAP N (2)

- Palace Lane, Beaulieu, SO42 7ZL
- 01590 612324   www.montaguarmshotel.co.uk
- SU387022   50.8183, -1.4516
- 1100-2300 Mo-Sa; 1100-2230 Su.

Ringwood: Best Bitter; two guests.

A handsome hotel, with four AA stars, two AA rosettes and one Michelin star. The building dates mainly from 1888, and was extended in the 20th century, but its origins were in the 1600s. There is much to excite the eye: oak floors, oak panelling, brick fireplace, beams, large conservatory, beautiful garden, the magnolia... Separate menus for restaurant and bar feature locally-sourced and free-range ingredients, and various versions of afternoon tea are served. Nearby are Beaulieu's Abbey and Motor Museum; Exbury Gardens and Bucklers Hard are each about three miles away.

BUCKLERS HARD
MASTER BUILDER'S HOUSE HOTEL

MAP J (15)

"The search for the perfect pint should last a lifetime."
MICHAEL JACKSON

- Bucklers Hard, SO42 7XB
- 01590 616253   www.themasterbuilders.co.uk
- SU408000   50.7972, -1.4216
- 1200-2300.

Ringwood: Best Bitter, seasonals.

The Master Builder's House is in a former shipbuilding village, source of many warships of Nelson's navy, whose terraces of Georgian cottages run down to the tranquil Beaulieu River on either side of the grass-verged and vehicle-free street. Its spacious bars are wood-panelled, beamed, wood- and tile-floored, and log-fired. Food, featuring local ingredients, is served in bar and restaurant. The village has a maritime museum, and nearby are the sights of Beaulieu, and the enormous ruined barn of St Leonard's Grange.

BATTRAMSLEY
HOBLER

MAP K (13)

- ⌨ Southampton Road, Battramsley, SO41 8PT
- ☎ 01590 623944   www.alcatraz.co.uk
- ↗ SZ306990   50.7904, -1.5661
- ⏰ 1100-2300.

◖❙ ✕ 🐟 ♿ ⛳ 🍽 ♨ P 🚌

🍺 Ringwood: Best Bitter; Timothy Taylor: Landlord.

"I was T.T. until prohibition."
GROUCHO MARX
1895–1977

The Hobler stands by the road between Brockenhurst and Lymington. It is popular with walkers, as a footpath passes the pub. The interior is a tasteful mix of traditional and contemporary décor, with comfortable leather seating complementing the original beams and wooden fittings. In addition to the main bar area there are three dining rooms. The home-cooked food, sourced locally, is served all day (until 9pm). Daily specials and Sunday roasts are served. The garden has an extensive, covered and heated decked area as well as grass. Free Wi-fi.

BOLDRE
RED LION

MAP K (20)

- ⌨ Rope Hill, Boldre, SO41 8NE
- ☎ 01590 673177   www.theredlionboldre.co.uk
- ↗ SZ318983   50.7837, -1.5493
- ⏰ 1100-1500, 1730-2300 Mo-Fr; 1100-2300 Sa-Su; longer hours Easter – September.

◖❙ S ✕ 🐟 🍴 ♿ ⛳ 🍽 ♨ P 🚌

🍺 Ringwood: Best Bitter, Fortyniner; Marston's: Pedigree; one guest.

The Red Lion dates back to the 15th century, and now incorporates original stables and old cottages. The interior feels cosy, with low beams, log fires and authentic décor. The pub has won awards for its home-cooked, locally-sourced food, which often includes game and seafood, and the home-made puddings are popular. Vice Admiral Lancelot Holland lived in the village, and was lost when HMS *Hood* was sunk by the *Bismarck*. St John's church, a mile northeast, contains a memorial to that ill-fated ship and her crew.

EAST END
EAST END ARMS

Lymington Road, East End, SO41 5SY
01590 626223   www.eastendarms.co.uk
SZ361967   50.7696, -1.4883
1100-1500, 1800-2330 Mo-Th; 1100-2330 Fr-Sa; 1200-2200 Su.

Ringwood: Best Bitter, Fortyniner; one guest.
Thatchers: Traditional.

The East End Arms is owned by a former bass player of *Dire Straits*. Its small public bar has a large open fire, and a counter that is wide enough for only two stools. The smart restaurant has a wood-panelled dado, and its walls are covered with pictures of the famous. Behind the counter are stillaged the ales and cider, served straight from the cask. The pub has a very good reputation for its food; the menu is varied and changes daily.

PILLEY
FLEUR-DE-LYS

Pilley Street, Pilley, SO41 5QG
01590 672158
SZ327982   50.7825, -1.5369
1200-2300 Mo-Sa; 1200-2230 Su.

Ringwood: Best Bitter; one guest.

This thatched pub claims to be the oldest in the Forest – there was an inn as early as 1096. It is part stone-floored, and the fireplace retains chains from which ham and fish were hung for smoking.

There is a small public bar, a lounge, and a snug with a farmhouse kitchen table. Food is served all day until 9pm, and the garden, with wishing-well and ornate birdhouse, hosts summer barbecues.

Thursday is quiz night; Saturday is Pudding and Pie Night. Boldre church, one mile north, contains the HMS *Hood* memorial.

WALHAMPTON
ELMERS COURT HOTEL

⌨ South Baddesley Road, Walhampton, SO41 5ZB
① 0844 879 9060   www.macdonaldhotels.co.uk/elmerscourt
↗ SZ336955   50.7593, -1.5255
🕐 1000-2200 Mo-Sa; 1100-2200 Su.

◖❚ S ✗ ⛷ ⛓ ⛄ ⬠ ⚙ ⌐ ♨ P ⇌

⌧ None

The principal building is a magnificent Victorian Tudoresque manor house; its many gables, bargeboards, mullioned and transomed windows, and tall chimneys present a visual feast. The Tudor Bar is wood-panelled, and furnished with armchairs. Sails Brasserie, a modern, nautically-themed bar, is open for breakfast; it is in a separate building that also contains a leisure club, a beauty spa, and a restaurant. The 42 luxury bedrooms are in three two-storey blocks. The complex is set in 23 acres of landscaped gardens beside the Lymington River.

WALHAMPTON
WAGGON & HORSES

⌨ Undershore Road, Walhampton, SO41 5SB
① 01590 672517
↗ SZ330957   50.7608, -1.5328
🕐 1200-2300 Su-We; 1200-2330 Th-Sa.

◖❚ S ✗ ⛷ ⛄ ⚙ ⌐ ♨ ⬠ Å P ⇌

⌧ Wadworth: Henry's IPA, 6X; up to two guests.

"A fine beer may be judged with only one sip, but it is better to be thoroughly sure."
CZECH PROVERB

The Waggon & Horses is an olde worlde country pub on the edge of Lymington, and very handy for the Isle of Wight ferry terminal. It has

Edwardian style leaded windows, and there are wagon (waggon?) wheels fitted into the partitions separating restaurant and bar. The menu is varied, and the home-cooked food may be enjoyed in either the restaurant or bar. On the second Monday of the month there is a folk music night, and quiz nights are held in winter.

WALHAMPTON
WALHAMPTON ARMS

MAP K (25)

🖃 Main Road, Walhampton, SO41 5RE
① 01590 673113   www.walhamptonarmslymington.co.uk
↗ SZ330965   50.7677, -1.5328
🕐 1100-1530, 1800-2300 Mo-Sa; 1200-2100 Su.
❶ ▶ S ☙ ⍾ 兯 ⟟ ⚙ ⌐ 艸 ∱ P

🍺 Ringwood: Best Bitter, Fortyniner; one guest.

This Grade II listed 19th century building, overlooking open countryside, was originally a model farm; it was converted to its current use in 1984. The building is single-storey, with tile-hung and pargetted gables, and set about a courtyard across which one must pass to enter the pub; above the entrance to the courtyard is a cupola dovecote. The interior is spacious and impressively beamed. The pub offers a main menu and, on Sundays and at lunchtimes, carvery options. There is live music on the last Friday of the month during summer.

BRAMSHAW
BRAMBLE HILL HOTEL

MAP C (2)

- ⌨ Bramshaw, SO43 7JG
- ☎ 023 8081 3165   www.bramblehill.co.uk
- ↗ SU261157   50.9407, –1.6301
- ⏱ 1200–2300 (summer); 1900–2300 Fr,
  1200–2300 Sa, 1200–1700 Su (winter).
- ◖❚ ✗ ⭢ 🐾 🛏 ❀ ⛟ P
- 🍺 Ringwood: Fortyniner; one guest.

"God made the wicked Grocer
For a mystery and a sign
That men might shun
the awful shops
And go to inns to dine."
REVD. SYDNEY SMITH
1771–1845

A former royal hunting lodge, with extensive grounds and noted for its collection of rhododendrons, flowering shrubs and trees. The hotel has been run by the same family since the 1980s. The building eschews symmetry in favour of a jumble of gables, dormers, bay windows, an oriel, and a pyramid-roofed water tower masquerading as a belvedere. The bar is warm and relaxing; it has panelled walls and a coffered ceiling, and is adorned with stag heads and antlers. The subterranean gents' toilet is worth a visit.

BROOK
BELL INN

MAP C (1)

- ⌨ Brook, SO43 7HE
- ☎ 023 8081 2214   www.bellinnbramshaw.co.uk
- ↗ SU272141   50.9258, –1.6139
- ⏱ 1200–2300.
- ◖❚ S ✗ ⭢ ♿ 🛏 ❀ ⌁ ⛟ P
- 🍺 Ringwood: Best Bitter; Timothy Taylor: Landlord; two guests.

The Bell dates from 1782 and retains many of its period features, but has the feel more of a modern hotel than a country pub. The bar is friendly and welcoming, and has an impressive central fireplace. Food is served all day; an extensive bar menu is available plus blackboard specials. The Bell is adjacent to

two 18-hole golf courses; for those who prefer watching to participation there is a large, flat-screen TV in the lounge. Well-behaved children are welcome; dogs are welcome only in the large garden.

BROOK
GREEN DRAGON
MAP C (4)

⬚ Brook, SO43 7HE
☎ 023 8081 3359   www.greendragonbedbreakfast.co.uk
↗ SU273140   50.9254, -1.6126
🕐 1100-1500, 1700-2300.

🍺 Ringwood: Best Bitter, Fortyniner; one guest.

A traditional country pub, refurbished in 1993 without losing any of its charm. Open-plan but retaining a cosy feel with low, beamed ceilings, open fires, and plenty of seating areas. Traditional food is served, along with a good selection of specials. No food Sunday evenings. A 'Meal Deal', offering three courses for four persons is available Monday to Thursday; booking is recommended. Well-behaved children and dogs are welcome. Adjacent to the car park are a small patio, with covered smoking area, and a garden.

FRITHAM
ROYAL OAK
MAP C (7)

⬚ Fritham, SO43 7HJ
☎ 023 8081 2606
↗ SU232141   50.9262, -1.6711
🕐 1100-1530, 1800-2300 Mo-Fr; 1100-2300 Sa; 1200-2300 Su.

🍺 Bowman: Wallops Wood ('Royal Oak'); Flack Manor: Double Drop; Ringwood: Best Bitter; up to four guests.

This small and ancient thatched pub serves beer direct from casks stillaged behind the counter of the main bar. The cosy adjoining room has an impressive fireplace and a small library; beyond that room is one of more modern appearance with service through a hatchway. Beware of low beams and head-cracking lintels. There is an ample garden and a pound for visiting horses. Locally-sourced ingredients feature in the excellent, simple lunches. Nearby Eyeworth Pond provided water for a gunpowder factory, a post box for which survives near the pub.

BRANSGORE
CARPENTER'S ARMS

MAP O (1)

🖃 103 Burley Road, Bransgore, BH23 8BA
☏ 01425 672295   www.fullers.co.uk/rte.asp?id=4&itemid=46&task=View
↗ SZ182975   50.7769, -1.7422
🕐 1130-2330.

◖❿ S ✕ 🐾 ✝ ⅙ ⑄ ⚊ ⚒ Å P 🚌

🍺 Fuller's: London Pride, Gale's HSB, ESB; Ringwood: Best Bitter.

The building dates from 1853, when it was erected by George Harris, a carpenter. It became a pub after the original owners fell into debt, and is now a large, open-plan bar and restaurant, the latter being in an extension added in 1984. At the back are a covered patio and a small children's play area. There is also some seating at the front. Food is served all day, consisting of traditional pub fare including steaks and fish. There is a pool table, darts and sports TV.

BRANSGORE
CROWN INN

MAP O (2)

🖃 Ringwood Road, Bransgore, BH23 8AA
☏ 01425 672279   www.vintageinn.co.uk/thecrownbransgore
↗ SZ187979   50.7806, -1.7349
🕐 1130-2330 Mo-Sa; 1130-2230 Su.

◖❿ S ✕ 🐾 ⅙ ⑄ ⚊ ⚒ Å P 🚌

🍺 Ringwood: Best Bitter; four guests.

The original two-bar pub is now part of the seating area with original floorboards; the current bar is in an extension. It is divided into several areas internally, elegantly furnished, dadoed and beamed, and has a

large and spacious garden. Weekly events include Monday's quiz night, Wednesday's grill night, and Friday's fish night, and there is occasional live music. The pub has a large car park and a grassed garden with many picnic benches. The village war memorial stands opposite.

BRANSGORE
THREE TUNS

MAP O (5)

- Ringwood Road, Bransgore, BH23 8JH
- 01425 672232   www.threetunsinn.com
- SZ190976   50.7778, −1.7314
- 1130−2300 Mo−Sa; 1200−2230 Su.

◖D S ✕ ➴ 🛉 🕭 ⛯ ⛱ ⇌ ⚏ ⚓ P ⊟

- Otter: Bitter; Ringwood: Best Bitter, Fortyniner; Timothy Taylor: Landlord; one guest.

This beautiful, thatched 17th century building was originally a farmhouse; it was converted into a pub in the early 1900s and subsequently extended. The snug has beams, flags and exposed brick; the lounge and restaurant are less spartan and more carpeted. The elegant terrace is bounded by shrubbery, and the garden offers views of fields, trees and sky. Food, which has won awards from *Egon Ronay* and the *AA*, is of high quality and makes much use of local ingredients; the menu is extensive without resorting to wild exoticism. Occasional live music.

HINTON ADMIRAL
CAT & FIDDLE

MAP H (1)

- Lyndhurst Road, Hinton Admiral, BH23 7DS
- 01425 276050   www.harvester.co.uk/find-a-harvester/thecatfiddlehintonadmiral.html
- SZ204952   50.7563, −1.7109
- 1100−2300 Mo−Sa; 1200−2230 Su.

◖D S ✕ ➴ 🕭 ⛯ ⛱ ⚏ 🜨 P ⇌ ⊟

- None

The Cat & Fiddle is recorded in the *Domesday Book* as a hospice run by the monks of Christchurch Priory; it still serves food and drink to the traveller, but now as a Harvester Salad & Grill. The single-storey, thatched building has been extended at both ends to form a U-shaped building containing a large restaurant and with a long bar set under a heavily-beamed ceiling. Outside is a large patio. Food is standard Harvester fare.

HINTON ST MICHAEL
CONQUEROR INN

MAP H (4)

⌧ East Close Hotel, Lyndhurst Road, Hinton St Michael, BH23 7EF
☎ 01425 672404   www.eastclose.com
↗ SZ214969   50.7718, –1.6966
🕐 1000–2300.

◖◗ S ☎ 🛏 ♿ 🛌 ⚙ ⚓ ⚒ P

🍺 Flack Manor: Double Drop; Ringwood: Best Bitter, seasonals.

The Conqueror and East Close Hotel were reopened recently after extensive refurbishment; the original buildings date from early Georgian times. This gastro-pub, named after William the Conqueror, who created the New Forest in 1079, has an elegant bar with leather sofas and an impressive open fireplace, and offers a sophisticated food menu. Ingredients are mainly locally-sourced, including from the hotel grounds. The hotel has 11 bedrooms, library, cocktail bar, gallery room and tea room, and the grounds feature a children's assault course and several references to *Alice in Wonderland*.

Memorial marking the Forest's contribution to WWII's air war, Holmsley (Bransgore)

BREAMORE
BAT & BALL

MAP B (1)

Salisbury Road, Breamore, SP6 2EA
01725 512252 www.thebatandballinn.co.uk
SU158178 50.9598, -1.7751
1200-2300 (2230 Su).
S P
Wells and Young's: Courage Best; one guest.

"I envy people who drink. At least they know what to blame everything on."
OSCAR LEVANT IN 'HUMORESQUE'

A Victorian building with impressive gables, and stone window surrounds and mullions. The part wood-panelled interior is divided into three distinct areas (for drinkers, diners and games-players), and has a small display of cricketing memorabilia. The pub has fishing rights on the Avon, and offers accommodation for up to eight in a lodge. No evening meals on Sundays and Mondays from November to February. Nearby are the Elizabethan Breamore House and its Countryside Museum, the Anglo-Saxon St Mary's church and, a mile's walk north-west of these, a mizmaze. Live music and quizzes feature monthly.

Breamore House

BROCKENHURST
BALMER LAWN HOTEL

MAP I (1)

- ✉ Lyndhurst Road, Brockenhurst, SO42 7ZB
- ☎ 01590 623116   www.balmerlawnhotel.com
- ↗ SU304032   50.8272, -1.5705
- ⏱ 1000-2300.

◖❱ S ✗ ➵ ⛏ ♿ ⛑ ❀ ⛺ P ⇌ ⛟

- 🍺 None

This 4* hotel was built as a private house and hunting lodge early in the 1800s and converted to its current use around 1850. Bar food is served all day, and jazz accompanies Sunday lunchtimes. There are 54 en-suite rooms, and many recreational and relaxational facilities. During World War I the hotel served as part of the New Zealand General Hospital, and during World War II as an Army Staff College. The graves of 93 ANZAC soldiers lie in the parish church's New Zealand Cemetery.

BROCKENHURST
BROOKLEYS

MAP I (2)

- ✉ 58 Brookley Road, Brockenhurst, SO42 7RA
- ☎ 01590 624625   www.brookleysbistro.com
- ↗ SU298022   50.8192, -1.5784
- ⏱ 0900-1430, 1800-2100 Tu-Th; 0900-1500, 1800-2130 Fr-Sa.

◖❱ S ✗ ➵ ♿ ❀ ⇌ ⛟

- 🍺 None

This converted shop in the centre of the village is based on an original Victorian private house. The small bar is in the older part of the building and is available to customers who are not eating. The bistro, in the modern extension at the front, offers classic food with modern touches. The outdoor, paved dining area is between the main building and the road. There is a public car park immediately behind the bistro.

BROCKENHURST
FOREST PARK HOTEL

MAP I (9)

Rhinefield Road, Brockenhurst, SO42 7ZG
01590 622844   www.forestparkhotel.co.uk
SU292026   50.8225, -1.5857
1100-2300.

Ringwood: Best Bitter; two guests from Marston's Beer Company.

A large, Tudoresque hotel on the opposite side of the village from the station; many-gabled, turreted, and with a handsome entrance porch. There are two contrasting bars: the public, with its sports televisions, is popular with locals; the quiet cocktail bar is favoured for pre-dinner drinks when visiting the large restaurant. The three acre garden contains a swimming pool and tennis courts. The hotel stands beside the road leading to Rhinefield Ornamental Drive.

BROCKENHURST
FORESTERS ARMS

MAP I (7)

10 Brookley Road, Brockenhurst, SO42 7RR
01590 623397   www.newforestonline.biz/forestersarms
SU302021   50.8183, -1.5727
1100-2400 Mo-Sa; 1130-2400 Su.

Fuller's: London Pride; Ringwood: Best Bitter, Fortyniner.

A sturdy, traditional Victorian pub; red brick with pale brick quoins, patterned roof tiles, and sash windows under segmental, brick arches. There are two bars – a lively public (with sports television), and a quieter lounge. The pub serves reasonably-priced food (snacks and full meals) throughout the day. The main outdoor drinking area is paved and next to the road, but there is also a small garden. The August bank holiday music festival is lubricated with a choice of ten or more real ales and ciders.

BROCKENHURST
LE BLAIREAU (CAREYS MANOR HOTEL)

MAP I (12)

- Careys Manor Hotel, Lyndhurst Road, Brockenhurst, SO42 7RH
- 01590 623032   www.blaireaus.com
- SU302027   50.8231, -1.5715
- 1000-1400, 1830-2145.

⊲❚ S ✗ ☞ ♿ ⌂ ❀ ⛺ P ⇌ 🚌

⌨ None

Le Blaireau is a French bistro, part of the large complex that is Careys Manor Hotel. The hotel offers accommodation, a spa, and two further restaurants: the Zen Garden (Thai), and the Manor; the latter has two AA rosettes and serves British food with a French influence. French occasions such as Bastille Day are celebrated with special events in Le Blaireau. Dogs are not allowed in the buildings, but there is an extensive, sheltered, outdoor eating and drinking area.

BROCKENHURST
RHINEFIELD HOUSE HOTEL

MAP I (18)

- Rhinefield Road, Brockenhurst, SO42 7QB
- 01590 622922   www.handpickedhotels.co.uk/
  hotels/rhinefield-house
- SU264036   50.8317, -1.6254
- 0930-2400.

⊲❚ S ✗ ☞ ♿ ⌂ ❀ ⛏ P

⌨ None

"If die I must, let me die drinking in an inn."
WALTER MAP
1140–1209

Beautiful Rhinefield House, standing in 40 acres at the south end of the Ornamental Drive, was built in the 1880s; it became a hotel in 1982. The exterior is Tudor-Gothic, with crenellations, mullions, transoms, galleries... Within are the Alhambra room, a hammer-beamed hall, Venetian glass, a carving of the Armada... Food is available in the restaurant,

and all day in the brasserie – the cream teas are recommended. The Ornamental Drive has many non-native trees. It is at its most beautiful in late May and early June, but delightful at any time.

BROCKENHURST
ROSE & CROWN

MAP I (19)

Lyndhurst Road, Brockenhurst, SO42 7RH
01590 622225   www.rosecrownpubbrockenhurst.co.uk
SU302023   50.8203, -1.5717
1100-2300 Mo-Sa; 1200-2230 Su.

Ringwood: Best Bitter, Fortyniner; two guests from Marston's Beer Company.

A traditional Forest pub built in the 1700s and extended in subsequent centuries. The façade comprises the original four bays and a Victorian cross-wing at either end; sash-windowed, dormered and part tile-hung. Accommodation is provided in 14 rooms. The restaurant is separate from the large main bar, and the skittle alley can be used for its ascribed purpose or be hired for other functions. The menu includes locally-sourced and New Forest Marque ingredients. Sunday night is quiz night. Disabled access is to the restaurant only.

BROCKENHURST
SNAKECATCHER

MAP I (20)

Lyndhurst Road, Brockenhurst, SO42 7RL
01590 622348   www.thesnakecatcher.co.uk
SU302022   50.8186, -1.5720
1100-2330 Mo-Sa; 1200-2230 Su.

Ringwood: Best Bitter, Fortyniner; seasonal beers from Marston's Beer Company.

"A quart of ale is a dish fit for a king"
SHAKESPEARE,
'THE WINTER'S TALE'

The Snakecatcher is named after the legendary Harry 'Brusher' Mills, who lived just north of Hollands Wood campsite (¾ mile north), and claimed to have a cure for rheumatism. The pub has separate pub games, bar and restaurant areas, and outdoor seating to the side and rear. The varied menu is served throughout the day, and specializes in 'hot rocks', on which you cook your own steak to your liking at the table. Ringwood Best is badged as Snakecatcher. Free Wi-Fi upon request.

SETLEY
FILLY INN

MAP I (6)

Lymington Road, Setley, SO42 7UF
01590 623449   www.fillyinn.co.uk
SU302002   50.8014, -1.5723
1100-2300 Mo-Fr; 1100-2400 Sa; 1200-2300 Su.

Ringwood: Best Bitter, Fortyniner; Shepherd Neame: Spitfire

The Filly Inn is an attractive 16th century country inn. Its hipped roof, decorative shutters and summer flowers add to its character. Inside, the large main fireplace and original wooden beams give it a cosy feel. The home-cooked menu is complemented by themed food nights and Sunday roasts. B&B accommodation is available. The pub is opposite Setley Plain, a popular heathland walking area. Dogs are welcome in the front part of the pub.

A memorial to Portuguese troops stationed here in WWI.

BURLEY
BURLEY INN

🖃 The Cross, Burley, BH24 4AB
① 01425 403448   www.theburleyinn.co.uk
↗ SU210030   50.8266, -1.7021
🕐 1100-2400 Mo-Sa; 1200-2300 Su.
   ◖❱ S ☕ 🐕 🦮 🚌 ⛲ ⌨ ♨ P ⊟

🍺 Ringwood: Best Bitter, Fortyniner, Old Thumper; one guest (summer only).

This Victorian pub, originally named the Toad Hole, is located in the lee of a hill in the centre of Burley – known as the 'Witches' Village'. The wooden turnstiles at the pedestrian entrance are there to prevent ponies and other animals from entering. The pub has a single bar with a cosy atmosphere and low-level background music. There is outdoor seating at the front, with an attractive covered terrace to the side. Food is served all day, and consists of traditional pub fare and various specials. Accommodation consists of ten bedrooms.

BURLEY
BURLEY MANOR HOTEL

🖃 Ringwood Road, Burley, BH24 4BS
① 01425 403522   www.theburleymanorhotel.co.uk
↗ SU211034   50.8300, -1.7014
🕐 1100-2300 Mo-Sa; 1200-2230 Su.
   ◖❱ S ✗ ☕ 🐕 🦮 🚌 ⛲ P ⊟

🍺 None

This grand manor house with intricate brickwork was built in 1852 as part of the Burley Estate. It became a hotel in 1932, when a new wing was added for the restaurant and extra bedrooms. There is a small bar with a spacious lounge which is open to the public, but it has no real ale. The bar offers reasonably priced food, however the restaurant is open only to residents and those who have booked. Deer roam in the field at the front of the hotel.

BURLEY
NEW FOREST CIDER

MAP G (3)

- Littlemead, Pound Lane, Burley, BH24 4ED
- 01425 403589   www.newforestcider.co.uk
- SU209027   50.8237, -1.7039
- 1000-1800 Easter - October; 1000-1700.
  November - Christmas, February - Easter.
- None
- New Forest: Sweet, Medium, Dry, Kingston Black.

"Yes, cider and tinned salmon are the staple diet of the agricultural workers."
EVELYN WAUGH
1903–1966

The shop is in a building behind the Forest Tea Rooms. Samples of the draught ciders (sold under the brand name Snake Catcher) are served from wooden casks, and bottled cider, perry, country wine and apple brandy are available. Most of the cider-making equipment is in the next-door barn, as is a small art gallery. A steam engine is employed in mid-October's cider-pressing weekend to make cider in the traditional way using local apples; the cider is matured in whisky barrels. Bed and breakfast is available in the farmhouse, with self-catering accommodation in the neighbouring cottage.

BURLEY
QUEEN'S HEAD

MAP G (4)

- The Cross, Burley, BH24 4AB
- 01425 403423   www.queens-head-pub-ringwood.co.uk
- SU211030   50.8268, -1.7009
- 1100-2300.
- Greene King: IPA; Ringwood: Best Bitter, Fortyniner; up to two guest beers.

A large pub with a single, L-shaped bar and three real fires. Earliest records show it in 1753 as the Booth's Arms. It has many cosy alcoves and small rooms in which to drink or eat, and there is an extensive outdoor seating area. Separate lunch and dinner menus offer quality fare, including an extensive vegetarian / vegan menu. Wheelchair access is to part of the pub only, and suitably equipped facilities are provided by the adjacent public toilets. The pub was visited by Glenn Miller shortly before his disappearance.

BURLEY
WHITE BUCK INN

MAP G (5)

⌨ Bisterne Close, Burley, BH24 4AT
☎ 01425 402264   www.fullershotels.com/rte.asp?id=128
↗ SU223027   50.8236, -1.6839
🕐 1000-2300 Mo-Sa; 1100-2230 Su.

◖ S ✕ ⛱ 🍴 ♿ 🛏 🐾 ⚘ ⚑ 🚭 P

🍺 Fuller's: Gale's Seafarers, London Pride, Gale's HSB, two guests.

Picturesque country hotel with a large pub / restaurant on the ground floor. Built as an Edwardian country house, it served as a hospital in World War II, and was later converted to a hotel. The large garden has benches, a fountain and a children's play trail. Food is served all day; much use is made of local produce, including *New Forest Marque*. Every Thursday is jazz night, and there are occasional special events such as tribute bands and family days.

BARTLEY
HAYWAIN

MAP D (7)

- ⌧ Southampton Road, Bartley, SO40 2NA
- ☎ 023 8081 2243   www.crowncarveries.co.uk/find-us/thehaywain.html
- ↗ SU307132   50.9176, -1.5645
- 🕐 1100-2300 Mo-Sa, 1100-2230 Su.

  ◖❙ S 🐎 ♿ ❀ P 🚌

- 🍺 Greene King: IPA; Ringwood: Best Bitter.

The Haywain is located just southeast of the Bartley crossroads on the A336. The original building was probably Victorian, with later additions. Inside, the pub is open-plan, large and somewhat rambling. The pub is a Crown Carvery, a Mitchells & Butlers brand. The good-value carvery is a strong attraction, and the pub is often busy. Snacks are limited to the starters from the Carvery menu. There is a quiz on Thursday evenings, and Paultons Park is a strong local attraction for families.

CADNAM
BUTLER'S BAR (BARTLEY LODGE HOTEL)

MAP D (1)

- ⌧ Bartley Lodge Hotel, Cadnam, SO40 2NR
- ☎ 023 8081 2248   www.newforesthotels.co.uk/hotels/
                    bartley-lodge-hotel-cadnam
- ↗ SU298130   50.9165, -1.5772
- 🕐 1200-2300.

  ◖❙ S ✗ 🐎 🐴 🛏 ❀ ⌐ P 🚌

- 🍺 None

Bartley Lodge was built in 1759 as the hunting lodge for the founder of the New Forest Hounds. Charles Lyell, a famous early geologist, spent his childhood here. The lodge is now a 3* hotel with a small sports complex (for residents only); it is Grade II listed, stands in eight acres, and is reached by a private road. Most unusually, the bar contains a bank of (redundant) wine taps, presumably dating from when the lodge was still a lodge.

CADNAM
COACH & HORSES   MAP D (2)

✉ 11 Southampton Road, Cadnam, SO40 2NF
☎ 023 8081 3120   www.foxandhoundslyndhurst.co.uk
↗ SU300133   50.9190, -1.5735
🕐 1200-2300 Mo-Sa; 1200-2230 Su.

◖▸ S 🐎 ⚘ ♿ ⚙ 🍴 P 🚃

🍺 Flack Manor: Double Drop; Ringwood: Best Bitter, Fortyniner.

The Coach & Horses is a large, white building on the south side of the A336, Victorian in origin but with later additions. Outside are pleasant drinking areas and a well-equipped children's play area; the interior is open-plan, and has separate areas for locals, drinkers and diners. Home-cooked food is available all day, with lots of specials. The locals' area has a dart board, a pool table and a television. There is a pub quiz on the last Thursday of each month. Paultons Park is a nearby attraction for families.

CADNAM
SIR JOHN BARLEYCORN   MAP D (11)

✉ Old Romsey Road, Cadnam, SO40 2NP
☎ 023 8081 2236   www.alcatraz.co.uk
↗ SU291136   50.9211, -1.5871
🕐 1100-2300.

◖▸ S ✕ 🐎 ⚘ ♿ ⚙ 🚐 P 🚃

🍺 Ringwood: Best Bitter; one guest.

"And a few men talked of freedom, while England talked of ale."
G.K.CHESTERTON
1874–1936

This low, thatched building was originally three cottages. It stands close to the M27, in a cul-de-sac that was formerly the main road, and is possibly the oldest pub in the Forest. Inside are a small lounge and bar, with a restaurant at one end and a large lounge-cum-dining room at the other; there is also a small function room. The rooms are slate-floored, and furnished in modern wood and leather. Food is traditional and modern English, and snacks are available until 6pm. Paultons Park is nearby.

CADNAM
WHITE HART

MAP D (13)

🖻 Old Romsey Road, Cadnam, SO40 2NP
☎ 023 8081 2277   www.hcpr.co.uk/whiteharthamp
↗ SU295136   50.9216, -1.5810
🕐 1100-2300 Mo-Sa; 1100-2230 Su.

◖▶ S 🐎 ♿ 🐾 🍴 P 🚌

🍺 Flack Manor: Double Drop; two guests.

The White Hart was originally a coaching inn on a main route to the West Country. It is an imposing, cream-painted, brick building, with ornate chimneys, and a patterned, tiled roof with three dormers. The single bar is surrounded by many narrow rooms, well-furnished, and with grey wood-panelling and lots of old pictures. The secluded garden contains a skittle alley. Modern English food is served all day until an hour or less before closing time. There is a quiz every other Wednesday. Paultons Park and the Rufus Stone are nearby.

COPYTHORNE
EMPRESS OF BLANDINGS

MAP D (4)

🖻 Romsey Road, Copythorne, SO40 2PF
☎ 023 8081 2321   www.hall-woodhouse.co.uk/
                   pubs/pubsearch/pub/?id=66
↗ SU312152   50.9357, -1.5565
🕐 1100-2300 Mo-Sa; 1200-2230 Su.

◖▶ S 🐎 🐕 ♿ 🐾 🍴 — 🍴 ▲ P 🚌

🍺 Hall & Woodhouse: Badger First Gold, Tanglefoot, seasonal.

A large pub named after a pig featured in a PG Wodehouse novel. Décor is traditional yet very light and welcoming, and the woody interior is spacious and well laid out, with small areas separated from the main space by screens. There are two wood burning stoves, and photos of the area adorn the walls. The menu includes pub classics, grills, vegetarian dishes, children's options, and daily specials. Fans of radio comedy should visit the toilets.

OWER
MORTIMER ARMS

MAP D (8)

🖾 Romsey Road, Ower, SO51 6AF
☎ 023 8081 4379   www.alcatraz.co.uk
↗ SU324164   50.9463, -1.5398
🕐 0700-2300.

◖ S ✕ ☕ 🛏 ❀ ᵎ ⚊ ♨ ⛺ P ☷

🍺 Ringwood: Best Bitter, Fortyniner.

"Always remember that I have taken more out of alcohol than alcohol has taken out of me."
WINSTON CHURCHILL

A solid-looking building with a slate roof, and a neat garden and patio. The pub has modern décor but retains a traditional feel, with log fire and handsome bar. Those wanting a drink or a snack will find ample space in the bar area, while those seeking a more substantial repast may wish to avail themselves of the restaurant. There are 14 en-suite bedrooms, and the pub, function room and accommodation can be hired for private parties. The Mortimer is on the doorstep of Paultons Park.

OWER
VINE INN

MAP D (12)

🖾 Romsey Road, Ower, SO51 6ZJ
☎ 023 8081 4333
↗ SU326170   50.9517, -1.5372
🕐 1100-2330 Mo-Fr; 1200-2330 Sa-Su.

◖ S ✕ ☕ 🛏 ❀ ᵎ ⚊ ♨ ⛺ P ☷

🍺 Greene King: IPA.

"There is nothing which has yet been contrived by man, by which so much happiness is produced as by a good tavern or inn."
SAMUEL JOHNSON

A large building beside the old Salisbury Road. The Vine is mainly set up as a restaurant serving a wide range of pub grub, but also has a separate bar area with beams and sofas. Flat-screen televisions show free-to-air channels. Children are well catered for here, and would love you to take them to nearby Paultons Park. Accommodation is available in the adjacent Premier Inn.

WINSOR
COMPASS INN

Winsor Road, Winsor, SO40 2HE
023 8081 2237   www.compassinn.co.uk
SU317143   50.9280, -1.5491
1200-2300.

◖◗ S ✗ ⛄ 🐴 ❀ ⌐ ⛰ ⛰ ♠ P 🚐

Fuller's: London Pride, Gale's HSB; Ringwood:
Best Bitter; Sharp's: Doom Bar.

*"The incognito of an inn is
one of its striking
privileges."*
WILLIAM HAZLITT
'ON GOING A JOURNEY'

A cosy and pretty village pub whose roof
is a mixture of styles, with a slate-roofed
extension. The interior has beams,
bare-brick walls, wooden floors,
wood-panelling and a handsome
fireplace. Seating includes a settle, and
plenty of interest is provided by the
many pictures and other adornments.
The whole is divided into bar, restaurant
and games area. The patio is sturdily
furnished, and its covered area provides
protection for smokers and those who
wish to admire the mural. Food, which includes children's options, is
available all day on Sundays.

*The Rufus Stone
with Sir Walter
Tyrrell's rather lame
excuse, Stoney Cross
(Minstead)*

DAMERHAM
COMPASSES

MAP A (4)

⌸ East End, Damerham, SP6 3HQ
☽ 01725 518231   www.compassesinndamerham.co.uk
↗ SU105161   50.9450, -1.8510
🕓 1130-1500, 1800-2300 Mo-Fr; 1130-2300 Sa; 1200-2230 Su.

◖ ▷ S ⛏ 🐂 ᕋ ♿ 🚪 ❀ ⛺ P

🍺 Ringwood: Best Bitter; Sharp's: Doom Bar; one guest.

This pub has been much extended since being built in Tudor times, and has at times had its own brewery, coach-house and dairy. There is a public bar, a spacious lounge/dining area, and a handsome conservatory; two real fires, agricultural equipment and many pictures worth studying add to the attraction. The garden affords verdant views. Food is available all day on Saturdays and Sundays; the menu includes home-made desserts and local artisan cheeses. Events include an annual casino night. Nearby, but remote from the village, is the 12th century parish church.

COMMONERS' RIGHTS

A Commoner is a person exercising the commoner's rights that attach to the land that he or she occupies. Qualifying land and property are recorded in the Atlas of Forest Rights, which is maintained by the Verderers.

A Commoner has some very ancient rights which date back almost a thousand years to William I's founding of his Royal Forest:

RIGHT OF COMMON OF PASTURE – Permitting the turning out onto the Forest for pasture of cattle, ponies, donkeys and mules.
RIGHT OF PANNAGE (also known as the Common of Mast) – Permitting turning out pigs into the wooded areas in autumn to feed on the acorns and beech mast.
RIGHT OF ESTOVERS – Permitting the gathering of firewood for personal use.
RIGHT OF TURBARY – Permitting the digging of peat for personal use.

ASHURST
NEW FOREST HOTEL

MAP D (9)

- ▭ Lyndhurst Road, Ashurst, SO40 7AA
- ☎ 023 8029 2721 www.fullers.co.uk/
  rte.asp?id=243&itemid=185&task=View
- ↗ SU333102 50.8906, -1.5273
- ⏱ 1100-2300 Mo-Sa; 1100-2200 Su.

◖◗ S ✕ ⛺ ★ ♿ ❀ ♨ Ⓐ P ⇌ ▭

- 🍺 Fuller's: London Pride, Gale's HSB, ESB, one guest.

This much-extended former hotel stands at the entrance to the rail station's car park. It has impressive chimneys, and an interior divided into numerous areas decorated in different styles. Dogs are welcome in the bar area, but not in the restaurant. Much of the menu has the *New Forest Marque* to indicate local produce, and is served all day on Saturday (until 9pm) and Sunday (until 8pm). The pub is close to the Ashurst campsite and has a children's play area in the large garden.

BEAULIEU ROAD
DRIFT INN

MAP E (3)

- ▭ Beaulieu Road, Beaulieu Road, SO42 7YQ
- ☎ 023 8029 2342 www.driftinn.co.uk
- ↗ SU350062 50.8549, -1.5037
- ⏱ 1100-2400 Mo-Sa; 1200-2230 Su.

◖◗ S ✕ ⛺ ★ ♿ 🛏 ❀ ♨ Ⓐ P ⇌ ▭

- 🍺 Fuller's: London Pride; Greene King: Abbot Ale; Ringwood: Best Bitter, Old Thumper; one guest.

"I'm only here for the beer."
ROS LEVENSTEIN

The former Beaulieu Road Inn is surrounded by heath. It takes its name from the annual New Forest 'drifts', in which ponies are rounded up for health checks, branding, marking, and perhaps sale; the holding pens for the sales are opposite the pub. The interior has dark wood furniture, comfortable chairs, leather settees and open fires. There is also a games area with pool and darts. The menu includes children's options, and accommodation is available in the adjoining hotel. Isolated, but convenient for Lyndhurst and Beaulieu.

DENNY LODGE

HILL TOP
ROYAL OAK

MAP J (17)

⌨ Exbury Road, Hill Top, SO42 7YR
☎ 01590 612228
↗ SU401032   50.8269, -1.4313
🕐 1100-2300 Mo-Sa; 1200-2230 Su.
◖▌ S ➹ ⌖ 🐾 ♿ ⚙ ⌣ ♨ P 🚌

🍺 Adnams: Broadside; Greene King: Abbot Ale; Ringwood: Best Bitter;
Wadworth: Bishop's Tipple; occasional guests.
🍎 Broadoak: Pheasant Plucker; Lilleys: Bee Sting

The Royal Oak stands in an area called Hill Top, and near the eponymous Farm, House and Wood; to avoid confusion it is known locally as 'The Hilltop'. Internally it is a single space with an open log fire sitting on flagstones. Outside there is a paved and covered smoking area, and a large, grassed area with picnic tables. The pub offers a convenient refreshment stop for those travelling between Beaulieu (Montagu Motor Museum, Abbey and other delights) and Exbury Gardens. There is a biannual beer festival.

HOLBURY
BRIDGE TAVERN

MAP J (2)

⌨ Ipers Bridge, Holbury, SO45 2HD
☎ 023 8089 2554   www.bridgetavern.co.uk
↗ SU424031   50.8260, -1.3986
🕐 1100-1500, 1700-2300 Mo-Fr; 1100-2300 Sa-Su.
◖▌ S ✕ ➹ ⌖ 🐾 ♿ ⚙ ⌣ ♨ ⚓ P 🚌

🍺 Ringwood: Best Bitter; Wychwood: Hobgoblin; up to four guests.

The core of this pub dates from the mid 18th century; the flat-roofed extensions from somewhat later. It has a small public bar and a separate lounge and restaurant. The menu includes venison and pheasant when in season. The Bridge is a good starting or finishing point for heath and woodland walks. Exbury Gardens is only two miles away, but the Forest's roads extend that distance to 3½ miles; beyond Exbury are the beauties of the Beaulieu River and the Solent coastline.

MARCHWOOD
BOLD FORESTER

MAP E (2)

⌨ Beaulieu Road, Marchwood, SO40 4UQ
☎ 023 8086 5967
↗ SU377085   50.8750, -1.4650
🕐 1145-2300 Mo-Sa; 1145-2230 Su.

◖▶ S ✗ ⌘ ♿ ❀ ⌁ P

🛏 Two guests.

"What two ideas are more inseparable than Beer and Britannia?"
REVD. SYDNEY SMITH
1771–1845

The original, modest, two-storey building shyly looks out from above the surrounding single-storey extensions. The Bold Forester is now a large pub with dining room, function room, skittle alley, and an outside children's play area with climbing frame and swings. The menu includes a Sunday carvery. The pub is two miles from the New Forest Wildlife Park, and a further mile from Longdown Activity Farm.

Otters at the New Forest Wildlife Park, Longdown (Denny Lodge)

EAST BOLDRE
TURFCUTTERS ARMS

Main Road, East Boldre, SO42 7WL
01590 612331   www.the-turfcutters-new-forest.co.uk
SU374004   50.8025, -1.4702
1100–2300 Mo-Sa; 1200–2230 Su.

Ringwood: Best Bitter, Fortyniner; two guests.

This brick-built, bargeboarded and bay-windowed building stands at the edge of Bagshot Moor. Its name records commoners' turbary rights, irons for the exercising of which are displayed within. The interior is cosy and rustic, with beams, stone floors, scrubbed tables, and fireplaces. The bar is usually alive with conversation, and two satellite rooms provide the more serene atmosphere favoured by diners. Accommodation is in three en-suite rooms in a former barn. Nearby attractions include Beaulieu, Bucklers Hard and the remains of Beaulieu Airfield, whose runway is now used only by model aircraft.

All Saints Church, Fawley (Fawley)

IBSLEY
OLD BEAMS INN

🖃 Salisbury Road, Ibsley, BH24 3PP
☎ 01425 473387 www.alcatraz.co.uk
↗ SU149094 50.8843, -1.7886
🕒 1100-2300 Mo-Sa; 1100-2230 Su.

◖▶ S ✖ 🐎 ♿ 🛏 ❀ ⚒ P 🚂

🍺 Greene King: IPA, Old Speckled Hen.

It has been alledged that in Great Britain alone, 163,215 pints of beer each year are lost in the moustaches and beards of beer drinkers.

Originally a small, thatched roadside inn, this food-oriented pub has been greatly extended and tastefully modernised. As only the original building is visible from the road, the size of the interior may surprise; the dining room can cater for large parties. A private dining room is also available, and can be hired for meetings. Guide dogs are welcome.

LINWOOD
HIGH CORNER INN

🖃 Linwood, BH24 3QY
☎ 01425 473973 www.highcornerinn.co.uk
↗ SU197107 50.8959, -1.7213
🕒 1100-1500, 1800-2300 Mo-Fr (winter); 1100-2300 Mo-Fr (summer); 1100-2300 Sa; 1100-2230 Su.

◖▶ S 🐎 🐈 🛏 ❀ ⚒ P

🍺 Wadworth: 6X; two guests from either Wadworth or Red Shoot.
🍏 Westons: Scrumpy.

This remote pub, tucked away at the bottom of a gravel track, has been in use since the 1700s. It has been much extended, features many rooms on different levels, offers accommodation in a separate block, and has a large, tree-shaded beer garden with a children's play area. Weddings are hosted in the function room. The area is popular with walkers, and provides several options for Forest pub crawls; the Red Shoot Inn, Brewery and campsite are about a mile away.

ELLINGHAM, HARBRIDGE AND IBSLEY

LINWOOD
RED SHOOT INN

MAP B (6)

Toms Lane, Linwood, BH24 3QT
01425 475792   www.redshoot.co.uk
SU187093   50.8835, -1.7352
1100-2300.

◖◗ S ⛄ ⛗ ♿ ⛲ ⌁ ⛺ ⚠ P

Red Shoot: two from New Forest Gold, Muddy Boot, Tom's Tipple; Wadworth: Henry's IPA, 6X, guests.

Set in a former farmhouse, this large inn opened in 1964. Six real ales are often available, at least two of which are brewed in-house by the Red Shoot Brewery, which can be viewed through a large glass window in the pub. Good pub food is served. A campsite is adjacent to the pub, and the remote location makes it popular with touring visitors and walkers. Live music features on Sunday nights, and beer festivals are held in April and October.

ROCKFORD
ALICE LISLE

MAP F (1)

Rockford Green, Rockford, BH24 3NA
01425 474700   www.fullers.co.uk/rte.asp?id=243&itemid=3&task=View
SU160080   50.8720, -1.7735
1000-2300 Mo-Sa; 1200-2230 Su.

◖◗ S ✂ ⛄ ⛗ ♿ ⛲ ⌁ ⛺ P

Fuller's: Gale's Seafarers, London Pride, Gale's HSB, one seasonal.
New Forest: at least one cider.

This spacious, well-appointed country inn is named after a local dame who was controversially sentenced to death by Hanging Judge Jeffreys for harbouring fugitives from the Monmouth rebellion. It is located on a green set back from the road, offers good pub food, and welcomes children until 9pm. The large beer garden features a children's play area, a large bird cage and views over the adjacent lake. It is especially popular in summer and is a good base for a pub walk.

BLACKFIELD
HAMPSHIRE YEOMAN

MAP J (8)

⌨ Hampton Lane, Blackfield, SO45 1XA
☎ 023 8089 8781
↗ SU442023   50.8188, -1.3727
🕐 1500-2300 Mo-We; 1500-2400
Th-Fr; 1200-2400 Sa; 1200-2230 Su.

🐕 🐎 ❀ ⌐ 🚌 P 🚍

🍺 None

"You can't be a real country unless you have a beer and an airline - it helps if you have some kind of football team, or some nuclear weapons, but at the very least you need a beer."
FRANK ZAPPA

This large local pub has one public room which has a U-shaped bar and a small, raised area. Entertainments available include a pool table, a dartboard and several sports televisions. Outside at the front are a few benches. Frequent music events are staged. The pub was built in the 1950s to serve workers employed on the rebuilding and extension of the nearby Fawley oil refinery, one of the largest in Europe, and providing 20% of the UK's refining capacity.

CALSHOT
SPINNAKER BAR

MAP M (3)

⌨ Sunderland Hangar, Calshot Activities Centre, Calshot, SO45 1BR
☎ 023 8089 1412
↗ SU488023   50.8184, -1.3078
🕐 1900-2300 Mo; 1200-1400, 1900-2300 Tu-Fr; 1200-2100 Sa;
1200-1700 Su. Closed mid-December to mid-January

◑ 🍴 🐕 🐎 ⌐ ❀ 🛠 P 🚍

🍺 Greene King: IPA.

This bar is in a former aircraft hangar, part of Calshot Activities Centre. Its shoreside garden affords views to the Isle of Wight and Portsmouth. Food, available until about one hour before closing time, includes Thai curries. Yards away is one of Henry VIII's castles, wherein one can learn of Calshot's military history, and its associations with the Schneider

Trophy, seaplanes, flying-boats and T.E. Lawrence. Also nearby is Calshot Marshes Nature Reserve. Beware of seasonal car parking charges; dogs in the garden only.

FAWLEY
FALCON

⌨ The Square, Fawley, SO45 1DD
☎ 023 8089 1005
↗ SU458032   50.8267, -1.3505
🕐 1100-2300 (2400 Fr)

◖ S 🐾 🎯 🛏 ✳ Å P 🚌

🍺 Ringwood: Best Bitter; two guests.

Tegestology is what collecting beer mats is called.

A Victorian building in red and yellow brick, imposing and square on Fawley's unsquare Square, and a short walk from the fine Norman parish church. The public bar has pool, darts and several televisions. The lounge is divided into two comfortable areas, with old photographs of the pub on

the walls, and images of falcons to remind the drinker of his whereabouts. Food is available from midday until 8pm daily. Regular events include steak nights, curry nights, and live folk music.

FAWLEY
JOLLY SAILOR

⌨ Ashlett Road, Ashlett Creek, Fawley, SO45 1DT
☎ 023 8089 1305
↗ SU465032   50.8269, -1.3400
🕐 1100-2300 Mo-Sa; 1200-2300 Su.

◖ S 🐾 🎯 ✳ ⛪ P 🚌

🍺 Ringwood: Best Bitter; one guest.

The Jolly Sailor stands at the end of Ashlett Creek, near a former granary and tide mill (now a sailing club). This tranquil location between refinery and power station is a good one from which to observe the nautical

activity on Southampton Water or enjoy a coastal walk to Calshot Marshes Nature Reserve. The original building has received several extensions; evidence without and photographs within tell some of the story of its development. Food includes homemade pies, and is available midday until 8pm (9pm Friday and Saturday).

FAWLEY

HARDLEY
FOREST HOME

MAP J (5)

⊡ Long Lane, Hardley, SO45 3FH
☎ 023 8084 2270   www.theforesthome.co.uk
↗ SU429048   50.8419, - 1.3914
🕐 1100-2300 Mo-Th; 1100-2330 Fr-Sa; 1200-2230 (2300 summer) Su.

◖❙ S ✗ ⛄ ♞ 🐕 ♿ ☸ ⌞ ⚰ ⚓ P 🚌

🍺 Fuller's: Gale's HSB; Ringwood: Best Bitter; one guest.

This angular edifice was built as a pub in 1879. It is near Fawley refinery and beside a busy road, but also on the Solent Way and frequented by horse-riders. The exterior is deeply-eaved and many-gabled (there appear to have been many extensions); the interior is open-plan but contains public bar and lounge / dining areas. Food, which includes Sunday roasts, makes use of local ingredients. There is a quiz on Thursday evenings, and the pub supports ladies' and men's darts teams, a cribbage team, and two football teams.

HOLBURY
HOLBURY INN

MAP J (11)

⊡ 63 Long Lane, Holbury, SO45 2LG
☎ 023 8089 0695   www.holburyinn.co.uk
↗ SU437037   50.8318, - 1.3803
🕐 1400-2300 Mo-Th; 1200-2400 Fr-Sa;
   1200-2230 Su.

⛄ ♞ 🐕 ☸ ⌞ ⚰ P 🚌

🍺 None

"Who comes here? A Grenadier.
What does he want?
A pot of beer."
CHARLES DICKENS
'OUR MUTUAL FRIEND'

The Holbury is a 1930s pub with two large bars. The public bar is called the 'Sports Bar'; sports include pool, darts and a punchbag. Sports television is shown and there is a wood-burning stove. The lounge is a more peaceful area, with a motor scooter theme; it has sofas, a poker table and an open log fire. At the rear is a large garden with benches and a children's play area. Wednesday night is quiz night, and there are frequent music events.

HOLBURY
OLD MILL INN

MAP J (16)

- ▣ Lime Kiln Lane, Holbury, SO45 2HE
- ☾ 023 8089 1137   www.theoldmillinn.org
- ↗ SU426040   50.8343, -1.3957
- ◷ 1200-2300 Mo-Th; 1200-2400 Fr-Sa; 1200-2230 Su.

◖▮ ⚞ ⛄ ⚲ ♿ ⛺ ⚘ ⚑ ━ ♨ P ⊟

- ◲ Fuller's: London Pride, ESB; Ringwood: Best Bitter; one guest.

At the edge of Holbury Purlieu (and handy for heathy walks) this old, rambling, part-thatched pub includes a mill worker's cottage and a timber-framed and herringbone-nogged barn. The interior is spacious and comfortable, with beams, a brick-built bar counter and a large fireplace. Outside there is a pretty, ornamental pond, and a large children's play-area. The barn serves as a function room and the venue for the frequent music events. Accommodation is in three nicely furnished rooms.

LANGLEY
LANGLEY TAVERN

MAP J (12)

- ▣ Lepe Road, Langley, SO45 1XR
- ☾ 023 8089 1402
- ↗ SU446010   50.8075, -1.3679
- ◷ 1100-2300 Mo-Th; 1100-2400 Fr-Sa; 1100-2300 Su.

◖▮ S ⚞ ⛄ ⚲ ♿ ⛺ ⚘ ⚑ ━ ♨ P ⊟

- ◲ Flack Manor: Double Drop; Ringwood: Best Bitter; two guests.

A large, brick-built and crowstep-gabled pub erected in the 1930s for Brickwoods Brewery. Following a period of closure, it was refurbished and reopened in 2009. The public bar is a venue for live music on most Friday and Saturday evenings. The lounge bar, comfortably furnished in a minimalist style, is popular with diners (no food Mondays). The pub is 1½ miles from Exbury Gardens (2½ by road), and 1½ miles from the coast at Lepe, with its Country Park and Luttrell's Tower (an 18th century folly now owned by the Landmark Trust).

ASHFORD
AUGUSTUS JOHN

MAP A (1)

- 116 Station Road, Ashford, SP6 1DG
- 01425 652098   www.augustusjohnfordingbridge.co.uk
- SU137143   50.9288, -1.8053
- 1130-1500, 1800-2300 Mo-Th; 1130-1500, 1700-2400 Fr; 1130-1500, 1800-2400 Sa; 1200-1500, 1900-2300 Su.

◖◗ S ✗ ⛏ ⊼ ☇ ⇔ ⚘ ⌵ ⚓ P ⊟

Ringwood: Best Bitter, Fortyniner; occasional seasonal and guest beers.

The Railway Hotel was renamed after closure of the line in 1964. The eponymous artist, who died in Fordingbridge in 1961, was a customer; prints of his work adorn the walls. The pub has a bar and a restaurant area, and the varied menu features locally-sourced produce, and includes vegetarian options, a children's menu and home-made desserts. Four rooms are available for accommodation but wheelchair access is to the pub only. Nearby are Rockbourne's Roman villa, the Avon Valley footpath, and good fishing.

BURGATE
TUDOR ROSE

MAP A (10)

- Burgate, SP6 1LX
- 01425 652227
- SU152156   50.9397, -1.7849
- 1200-2300.

◖◗ S ✗ ⛏ ⊼ ☇ ⚘ ⌵ P ⊟

Ringwood: Best Bitter, Fortyniner.

"The heart which grief hath cankered, Hath one unfailing remedy – the Tankard."
C.S.CALVERLEY 1831–1884

This thatched building originated as a pair of Tudor cottages and has been extended over the centuries. There is a central bar area, with dining areas on either side; food is home-cooked, and includes fish specials. There is a

separate games room with pool table and darts, and the young at heart will love the mini-golf course in the garden. Nearby Breamore House and Breamore's Saxon church are well worth a visit, and the Avon Valley footpath is but a few steps away.

FORDINGBRDGE
BUTLER'S

MAP A (2)

⌨ 1 Shaftesbury Street, Fordingbridge, SP6 1JF
☎ 01425 652099
↗ SU146141   50.9265, -1.7927
🕐 1100-2300 Mo-Fr; 1100-2400 Sa; 1200-2200 Su.
◖▷ S ⛷ 🐴 🎦 ⌣ 🚌

🍺 Ringwood: Best Bitter, seasonals.

Corner pub on the edge the of the town centre. Originally the Royal Arms Hotel, it is now a modern pub catering for sports-minded people, with pool, sports and 3D television, and supporting three darts teams. The pub is popular for its breakfasts, steaks and burgers, and there is a disco or live music once a month. Children are permitted in the bar only during the day. It is a few minutes walk from all of the local shops.

FORDINGBRIDGE
CROWN INN

MAP A (5)

⌨ 62 High Street, Fordingbridge, SP6 1AX
☎ 01425 652552
↗ SU147141   50.9267, -1.7922
🕐 1100-2300 Mo-Th; 1100-2330 Fr-Sa; 1200-1500, 1900-2230 Su.
◖▷ S ✕ 🐴 🛏 🎦 ⌣ 🏛 P 🚌

🍺 Ringwood: Best Bitter; one guest: Fuller's London Pride or Otter Ale.

This former coaching inn, close to the Town Museum and other local amenities, has an impressive staircase, and a bar top formed from a single piece of elm about seven metres long. Drinkers and diners in the main area are separated by a large fireplace, and there is also a small dining room; no food is served in winter. A quiz night is usually held on winter Sunday or Monday nights.

FORDINGBRIDGE
GEORGE

MAP A (6)

- 14 Bridge Street, Fordingbridge, SP6 1AH
- 01425 652040   www.georgeatfordingbridge.co.uk
- SU149142   50.9273, -1.7894
- 1000-2330 Mo-Sa; 1000-2230 Su.

◖❙ S ✗ ⛄ ↟ ⚐ ❀ ♨ P ⛟

Greene King: Morland Original Bitter, Old Speckled Hen.

This riverside inn, decorated in modern style internally, welcomes drinkers but is principally about food, which may be enjoyed within the building, in the conservatory and on the riverside terrace which affords a fine view of the 'Great Bridge'; the river has been spanned here since 1286. All food is home produced, and includes daily specials, pies being a favourite; smaller portions are available from the wide ranging menu. Fishing is popular in the area; it's only a ten minute drive to Rockbourne trout lakes.

FORDINGBRIDGE
SHIP INN

MAP A (9)

- 68 High Street, Fordingbridge, SP6 1AX
- 01425 654371   www.theshipinnfordingbridge.co.uk
- SU146141   50.9267, -1.7927
- 1100-2300 Mo-Th; 1100-2400 Fr-Sa; 1200-1500, 1900-2300 Su.

◖❙ S ✗ ⛄ ↟ ⚐ ⛁ ❀ ♨ P ⛟

Greene King: IPA, Old Speckled Hen, Abbot Ale, seasonals.

The New Inn was renamed in the 1980s. Its woody interior is divided into a cosy dining area and a larger bar area, and features bare floorboards, a fine old bar, and a gantry. Food specialities include steaks, grills and seafood; the landlord is very proud of the Café de Paris sauce. En-suite accommodation is provided in one twin and one double room. In the nearby church of St. Mary the Virgin is a memorial to James Alexander, the last man to be killed in a duel in England.

GODSHILL
FIGHTING COCKS

MAP B (2)

⌧ Godshill, SP6 2LL
☎ 01425 652462
↗ SU176149   50.9337, -1.7505
🕐 0900-2300 Mo-Sa; 0900-2230 Su.

◖ ▷ S ✕ ⛴ ⛺ ⛓ ♿ ❀ ⛰ ⚓ P

🍺 Ringwood: Best Bitter; three guests.
🍎 Westons: Old Rosie.

Coronation Street's Rovers Return is named in honour of veterans of the Boer War

The very family-friendly Fighting Cocks stands on the north-west edge of the New Forest, and is popular with walkers, cyclists, and visitors to nearby Sandy Balls holiday, camping and caravan park. Within are large dining areas and a smaller bar area. Although the vegetarian is not neglected, the carnivore is

especially well-served here as the landlord is a master butcher; sausages and burgers are home-made. Godshill pottery is but a few minutes' walk eastwards.

Fly Agaric (amanita muscaria) – poisonous and violently hallucinagenic

DOWNTON
ROYAL OAK

MAP L (10)

⌨ Christchurch Road, Downton, SO41 0LA
☎ 01590 642297 www.theroyaloakdownton.co.uk
↗ SZ269934 50.7401, -1.6198
🕐 1100-2230 Mo-Th; 1100-2330 Fr-Sa; 1200-2230 Su.

◖▶ S ✕ ⛺ 🐴 ♿ ❀ ⛏ ▲ P ➤

🍺 Ringwood: Best, Fortyniner; one guest.

This old pub has a single bar, four real fires, a large extension housing a restaurant area, and outdoor seating on the front and rear patios. The regular menu is augmented by more exotic food in the evenings, and food is available all day on Saturday and Sunday. Regular events include Thursday's curry night and Tuesday's quiz night. Children are permitted inside until 7pm, and dogs are permitted only in the bar area. It is a few minutes' walk to Downton Holiday Park, and one mile to the coast.

EVERTON
CROWN INN

MAP L (3)

⌨ Old Christchurch Road, Everton, SO41 0JJ
☎ 01590 642655 www.crowninneverton.co.uk
↗ SZ291940 50.7457, -1.5879
🕐 1200-1530, 1800-2300 Tu-Sa; 1200-1600, 1900-2230 Su.

◖▶ S ⛺ 🐴 ♿ ❀ ⌄ ⛏ ▲ P ➤

🍺 Greene King: Abbot Ale; Ringwood: Best Bitter; one guest.

The Crown combines old and new to produce a modern feel in a warm and friendly village pub. It has two bars, one of which is generally the preserve of diners, and at the back there is a small garden. The extensive menu is frequently changed. Fresh food is cooked to order and makes use of local produce; everything except the bread is home-made. A wide selection of fine wines is also available.

HORDLE
THREE BELLS

MAP L (13)

Silver Street, Hordle, SO41 0FN
01425 610625   www.brewersfayre.co.uk/restaurants/details/?id=3536
SZ267958   50.7616, -1.6215
1100-2300 Mo-Sa; 1200-2230 Su.

Hook Norton: Bitter; Wychwood: Hobgoblin.

The Three Bells is a village pub with a well-maintained mock Tudor façade, including a projecting central bay with porch. Inside is a large, L-shaped bar with plenty of seating, and a recent extension has added a large restaurant to the rear of the pub. Part of the Brewers Fayre chain, the pub shares its site with a 20 bedroomed (all en-suite) Premier Inn. Food, which is standard Brewers Fayre fare, is available all day, and Thursday night is Curry Night.

TIPTOE
PLOUGH INN

MAP L (8)

Sway Road, Tiptoe, SO41 6FQ
01425 610185
SZ256970   50.7725, -1.6374
1100-2300 Mo-Sa; 1200-2230 Su.

Ringwood: Best Bitter, Fortyniner; one guest.

"A woman drove me to drink and I never even had the courtesy to thank her."
W.C.FIELDS

The Plough began life as a farm in the 17th century; today it is a lovely country pub. The low, wood-ceilinged bar has cosy little alcoves and open fireplaces. Beyond a large old wine barrel is a raised dining room, with wooden, pitched ceiling, where you can choose from a varied menu. There is a beer garden at the rear, and beyond this a field for campers. Music and quiz nights are held in summer.

FROGHAM
FORESTERS ARMS

⌨ Abbotswell Road, Frogham, SP6 2JA
☽ 01425 652294
↗ SU172128   50.9151, -1.7556
🕐 1200-1500, 1800-2300 Mo-Sa; 1200-1500, 1900-2230 Su.

◖ ▮ S ✕ ⛢ ♞ ♿ ❀ ♨ ⚲ P

🍺 Wadworth: Henry's IPA, 6X, Bishop's Tipple, Old Timer; occasional guests.

This pub, standing at the edge of the National Park, is popular with walkers and holiday-makers, and is the occasional meeting place for the local Great Dane owners' club. It consists of a bar with a raised area at one end, and a separate restaurant; the wood-burning stove is very welcoming in the winter. Food is a mix of traditional and continental-style meals, with daily specials and seasonal game and seafood. The pub is open all day during Frogham Fair, which takes place on August bank holiday Saturday.

NORTH GORLEY
ROYAL OAK

⌨ Ringwood Road, North Gorley, SP6 2PB
☽ 01425 652244   www.theroyaloakgorley.com
↗ SU161119   50.9064, -1.7724
🕐 1000-2400 Mo-Sa; 1100-2000 Su.

◖ ▮ S ✕ ⛢ ♞ ❀ ↩ ⚲ P ▦

🍺 Adnams: Broadside; Ringwood: Best Bitter; Sharp's: Doom Bar.

A pub since 1820, this thatched building overlooking the village green was once a royal hunting lodge. Inside there are many original features, including an open fireplace and stone floors. The garden has a children's

play area, the bar has skittles, and there is live music every Friday. Food from the wide-ranging menu is available lunchtimes and evenings every day, and features local game and other local produce when available. The flooded gravel pits that form nearby Blashford Lakes are now a nature reserve and water sports facility.

STUCKTON
THREE LIONS

Stuckton, SP6 2HF
01425 652489   www.thethreelionsrestaurant.co.uk
SU160134   50.9199, –1.7738
1200–1600, 1900–2300 Tu–Sa; 1200–1600 Su.

One beer from a local brewery.

Built in the 1600s as a farmhouse, extended over the years, with a large conservatory, this building houses a highly acclaimed restaurant. Accommodation is also offered. The small bar area is just inside the main entrance, and there are two comfortable dining areas wherein to enjoy seasonal food from local suppliers, including seafood and New Forest game; there is also an extensive wine list. Beer is served from polypins, usually from Ringwood Brewery but sometimes from another local brewery.

Pony grazing near the Royal Oak, North Gorley (Hyde)

HYTHE AND DIBDEN

DIBDEN
WATER'S EDGE

MAP J (20)

- Dibden Golf Centre, Main Road, Dibden, SO45 5TB
- 023 8084 5060   www.newforest.gov.uk/index.cfm?articleid=8147
- SU400080   50.8703, -1.4318
- 1100-1900 winter; 1100-2200 summer.

Ringwood: Best Bitter; Wells and Young's: Courage Best Bitter.

This building, near the eastern edge of the National Park, is part of Dibden Golf Centre, and therefore opens early to provide breakfasts for players. It was built in the early 1970s, has a large bar and dining area, a comfortable lounge, and a function room which may be hired for the celebration of weddings, anniversaries, and other rites of passage. The patio has panoramic views over Southampton Water. Nearby is Dibden church, which was bombed in 1940 and reopened in 1955 following restoration.

DIBDEN PURLIEU
GLENEAGLES

MAP J (7)

- Butts Ash Lane, Dibden Purlieu, SO45 3RF
- 023 8084 2162
- SU419058   50.8507, -1.4054
- 1100-2330 Mo-Sa; 1200-2230 Su.

Fuller's: Gale's HSB; Ringwood: Best Bitter; guests.

The Gleneagles was originally a house. Bought by Strong's brewery in 1961, it opened as the Jester but owes its current name to the long-serving landlord's enthusiasm for golf. The pub has darts, cribbage and pétanque

teams, and regular attractions include Sunday quizzes, monthly music quizzes, poker tournaments, and televised sporting events. The regular menu and specials are augmented on Wednesday's curry night and Friday's fresh fish night. The large garden, where dogs on leads are welcome, has a children's play area, and there is a heated smoking area.

DIBDEN PURLIEU
HEATH

Beaulieu Road, Dibden Purlieu, SO45 4PW
023 8084 2275
SU411059   50.8510, –1.4172
1100-2300 Mo-Sa; 1200-2230 Su.

◖ ▌ S ✕ ⛵ ♿ ❀ P ⊟

Ringwood: Best Bitter; Wadworth: 6X; one guest.

Over 100 years old, but several times extended and refurbished, the Heath stands just outside the National Park, on the edge of greater Hythe and across the road from Beaulieu Heath. The triangular bar fronts a well-furnished seating area; the standard menu of traditional pub fare, supplemented by a specials board, may be enjoyed here and in the restaurant. Alfresco seating is provided in the garden to the rear and on benches in front of the pub. The village of Beaulieu, with its many attractions, is three miles away.

HYTHE
BOATHOUSE HOTEL

29 Shamrock Way, Marina Village, Hythe, SO45 6DY
023 8084 4066   www.boathousehythe.co.uk
SU422083   50.8730, –1.4009
1100-2300 Mo-Sa; 1100-2230 Su.

◖ ▌ ✕ ⛵ ♿ 🛏 ❀ ⌁ P ⊟

Ringwood: Best Bitter.

A modern brasserie-style establishment located in Hythe Marina. The interior is open plan, with a screen separating bar and restaurant; outside there is a terrace overlooking the yachts in the marina. Food is modern in style, with separate menus for bar and restaurant, the latter's being different for lunch and dinner. Limited time free parking is permitted in the neighbouring public car park. On nearby Hythe Pier is the world's oldest pier railway, which carries foot passengers between the Southampton ferry and Hythe.

HYTHE
CROFT

MAP J (3)

⌨ Langdown Lawn, Hythe, SO45 5GS
☎ 023 8084 2141   www.the-croft.co.uk
↗ SU422070   50.8611, -1.4006
🕐 1100-2300 Mo-Sa; 1200-2230 Su.

◖▶ S ✕ ⛺ ⛭ ❀ ⌁ 🅼 P 🚌

🍺 Fuller's: London Pride; Ringwood: Best Bitter; one guest.

The Croft was a private dwelling until 1958, when it was purchased by Watney's brewery and converted into a public house. It has received numerous refurbishments, and now has a large and comfortably-furnished lounge, with log fire, and a light and airy dining area. The very large children's play area has a wooden tree house and climbing frame, and there is a covered smoking area. Live jazz is performed on the last Sunday of the month.

HYTHE
EBENEZERS

MAP J (4)

⌨ Pylewell Road, Hythe, SO45 6AR
☎ 023 8020 7799
↗ SU423080   50.8701, -1.4003
🕐 1130-1430, 1730-2300 Mo-Th; 1130-2300 Fr-Sa; 1200-2230 Su.

◖▶ S ⛭ ❀ ⌁ 🚌

🍺 Flack Manor: Double Drop; Greene King: Abbot Ale; one guest.

The name records the building's origin as a Baptist chapel. It was built in 1845, and saw service as a school and as a store for flour and furniture before becoming a pub in 1998. The bar is open-plan and modern, but with a traditional feel, and attracts seekers after conversation. Thai curries are available as well as more traditional, home-made pub food. Limited-time free parking is available behind the pub. Nearby, the world's oldest pier railway carries passengers between the Southampton ferry and the town.

HYTHE
FOUNTAIN COURT HOTEL

MAP J (6)

Frost Lane, Hythe, SO45 3NE
023 8084 6310   www.fountaincourthotel.co.uk
SU428064   50.8556, -1.3920
1100-2300 Mo-Sa; 1200-2230 Su.

Ringwood: Best Bitter; Greene King: Old Speckled Hen.

A former country house, white-painted and with quoins picked out in blue, this 24 bedroom hotel looks onto a patio and a lawned garden with children's play area and huge fountain, hence the name. The public bar has pool, darts and sports television; there is also a separate lounge / dining area, and a function room and skittle alley available for hire. The extensive menu embraces carvery options and children's choices. Regular events include karaoke on Thursday, live music on Friday and Saturday, and a quiz on Sunday.

HYTHE
HOBBITS

MAP J (10)

6B High Street, Hythe, SO45 6AH
023 8084 8524
SU423080   50.8703, -1.3992
1100-1430, 1900-2300 Mo-Th; 1100-2300 Fr-Sa;
1200-1500, 1800-2230 Su.

One guest.

A former off-licence, now a restaurant-cum-bar, Hobbits is part of a Georgian terrace. The handsome doorway and shop window enhance the exterior's attractiveness, and inside are (fake) beams and a bar area with a thatched roof. Additional seating is provided upstairs and on the traffic-free High Street. There are separate lunch and dinner menus, the latter offering a grander choice. An acoustic guitarist performs on Sunday evenings. Nearby, the world's oldest pier railway carries foot passengers to and from the Southampton ferry.

HYTHE
LORD NELSON

MAP J (13)

- 5 High Street, Hythe, SO45 6AG
- 023 8084 2169
- SU423080   50.8704, -1.3992
- 1100-2300 Mo-Th; 1100-2400 Fr-Sa; 1200-2300 Su.

  ◖▶ S ⌾ ㅖ ㅊ ὁ ❀ ㎡ ㋿

- Ringwood: Best Bitter; two guests.

The core of this pub is Georgian, and contains three small bars (Victory, Trafalgar and Poop Deck) and some original beams; these bars may be hired for functions. The fourth bar (Aft) is a recent addition, and the only room in which children are permitted. The garden, with hanging baskets, an anchor and a propeller, is an excellent location from which to observe the world's oldest working pier railway. Entertainment includes sport on five televisions, and live music on Friday or Saturday. Food is not served Friday to Sunday evenings.

HYTHE
MALT

MAP J (14)

- 43-45 South Street, Hythe, SO45 6EA
- 023 8084 2086   www.themaltpub.co.uk
- SU424076   50.8665, -1.3984
- 1700-2300 Mo-Th; 1700-0030 Fr; 1130-1530, 1830-0030 Sa; 1200-1530, 1900-2300 Su.

  ⌾ ㅖ ❀ ⌁ P ㋿

- None

A sturdy, Victorian building with a shallow, hipped roof, and bay windows either side of the front porch. The pub describes itself as an 'urban beach bar', a description emphasised by its cocktail menu and the surfboards and hammock suspended from the ceiling. The interior, with wooden floors and comfortable chairs, is divided into two public rooms: the front has a pool table; the rear has darts and television. There is a beer garden at the back, and the pub holds regular karaoke nights.

HYTHE
SEASHELLS

MAP J (18)

- 🖃 37 High Street, Hythe, SO45 6AG
- ☎ 023 8084 7188
- ↗ SU424079   50.8699, -1.3982
- 🕐 1000-2300 Su-Fr; 1000-2400 Sa.

  ◖ S ✕ ⛵ 🐾 ♿ P ⊞

- 🍺 Ringwood: Best Bitter, Fortyniner; one guest.

The Pilgrims landed at Plymouth Rock because of beer. They had planned to sail further south to a warmer climate, but had run out of beer on the journey.

The windows and terrace of this first-floor pub afford one of Hythe's best panoramic views of Southampton Water; binoculars hang near the windows. The open-plan interior includes an area usually dedicated to dining. Breakfast is served until midday, and the main menu, with carvery on Sunday, from midday until 9pm. There is a quiz on Monday night, and live entertainment on Friday and Saturday nights. Dogs may enjoy the terrace only, and cars may enjoy time limited free parking in the adjacent public car park.

HYTHE
TRAVELLERS REST

MAP J (19)

- 🖃 Hart Hill, Hythe, SO45 3ND
- ☎ 023 8084 2356
- ↗ SU430063   50.8553, -1.3895
- 🕐 1800-2330 Mo; 1200-1500, 1800-2330 Tu-Sa; 1200-2230 Su.

  ◖ S ⛵ 🐾 ♿ ♿ ⊱ P ⊞

- 🍺 Ringwood: Fortyniner; Sharp's: Doom Bar.

The pub stands in verdancy at the southeastern edge of town, on a single-track road that forms part of the Solent Way, and close to Hythe Spartina Marshes nature reserve. It was built as a cottage in the 1700s and, although extended and refurbished, still looks the part with its sash windows and pretty porch. The interior is modern, and the small garden has fine views over a narrow, grassy valley. The extensive menu

includes Sunday roasts. Events include Monday's meat draw, Tuesday's cribbage, Wednesday's poker, and Thursday's live music.

LANDFORD
LANDFORD POACHER

MAP C (6)

⌨ Pound Hill, Landford, SP5 2EE
☎ 01794 390353
↗ SU256202   50.9806, -1.6368
🕐 1100-2300 Tu-Sa; 1100-1600 (2300 summer) Su.

◖▶ S ✗ ⅀ ♞ ♘ ♿ ♣ ⚒ P 🚌

🍺 Black Sheep: Best Bitter; Ringwood: Fortyniner; Wychwood: Hobgoblin.

A large building on the A36, with half-hipped roof and dormers, the Landford Poacher enjoys both local and passing trade. Within, the bar and beams are decorated with pewter tankards, and free Wi-Fi is available. The pub has a large restaurant offering home-cooked food, much of it sourced from local suppliers, and hosting themed events such as curry and steak nights. There is a separate bar snacks menu, and on Sundays two roasts are offered, one of which is always beef.

BOWLING GREEN
WHEEL INN

MAP L (14)

⊞ Sway Road, Bowling Green, SO41 8LJ
① 01590 676122   www.thewheelinnpub.co.uk
↗ SZ297966   50.7687, -1.5796
⏱ 1100–2400 Mo–Th; 1100–0100 Fr–Sa; 1200–2300 Su.

⊞ Ringwood: Best Bitter; two guests.

This Victorian building, in the middle of the road junction, was originally a pottery, then a blacksmith's. Meals (no snacks) are available only in the pub's Thai restaurant; food is served lunchtimes and evenings from Tuesday to Sunday and on bank holidays. The bar has music and a large television; the restaurant is quieter. When the restaurant is closed on Mondays it is used for an acoustic singaround, and there is stand-up comedy on the second Tuesday of the month.

LYMINGTON
4 SAIL

MAP K (1)

⊞ Anchor House, Bath Road, Lymington, SO41 3YL
① 01590 677705   www.finefood4sail.co.uk
↗ SZ329953   50.7570, -1.5345
⏱ 0900–2300 Tu–Th; 0900–2330 Fr–Sa; 1000–1600 Su.

⊞ Fuller's: London Pride.

This delicatessen-cum-brasserie was formed from the combination of four office units. It has a small bar and backs onto Lymington Yacht Club. The interior is modern, with large wooden tables and sailing décor. Separate menus for breakfast, lunch and dinner; in addition, cooking may be performed on 'hot rocks' on

Wednesday to Saturday nights. Part of the dining area is available for functions. The business provides a takeaway service for visiting yachts, and offers free computer access to the internet.

LYMINGTON
ANGEL

MAP K (2)

⬚ 108 High Street, Lymington, SO41 9AP
☎ 01590 672050   www.angelpublymington.co.uk
↗ SZ324955   50.7587, -1.5407
🕐 1100-2300 Mo-Sa; 1200-2230 Su.

◖▮ S ✕ ⟐ ♿ ⛐ ❀ ⛺ ≈ ⊟

🍺 Marston's: Pedigree; Ringwood: Best Bitter, Fortyniner; one guest.
🍎 Thatchers: Green Goblin.

In 1300 the George Inn stood here; the Angel is recorded in 1756 as a coaching inn. The façade is adorned with a pretty, cast iron balcony spread across five first-floor bays. The beamed interior is divided into a number of areas, all served from a U-shaped bar. To the rear of the pub is a patio. Food is served all day, and non-alcoholic refreshment is available from 9am. Numerous ghostly visions have been reported, resulting in the Angel's appearance in Jack Hallam's *Haunted Inns of England*.

LYMINGTON
BOROUGH ARMS

MAP K (3)

⬚ 39 Avenue Road, Lymington, SO41 9GP
☎ 01590 672814
↗ SZ322958   50.7614, -1.5447
🕐 1600-2300 Mo; 1100-2300 Tu-Th; 1100-2400 Fr-Sa; 1200-2230 Su.

S ⟐ ❀ ╘ ⛺ P ≈ ⊟

🍺 Ringwood: Best Bitter, Fortyniner; guests.
🍎 Westons: Old Rosie; one guest.

This lively community pub is a former post house, built in 1855. The frontage is red brick with yellow brick quoins, two porches, sash windows, and a central bay window with stained glass representations of the four seasons. A single bar serves a wooden-floored room which offers entertainment in the form of darts, pool, a juke box and televised sport. Adjoining is a carpeted lounge area for quiet conversation. Bar snacks are generally available throughout the day. The rear patio and a few benches at the front provide outside seating.

LYMINGTON
BOSUN'S CHAIR

MAP K (4)

Station Street, Lymington, SO41 3BA
01590 675140 www.bosunschairlymington.co.uk
SZ326957 50.7607, -1.5382
1800-2400 Mo-Th; 1200-2400 Fr-Su; 1200-2400 (summer).
Wadworth: Henry's Original IPA, 6X, seasonal.

This three-storey building was originally a coach house. The façade has striking stone-surrounded windows. The single bar, which has a dining area on one side, is decorated with boating memorabilia. Outside are a paved patio area and a long, narrow, decorative garden with tables and chairs. Food includes local handmade pies, and a barbecue menu in summer. Entertainment includes televised sport, darts, monthly live music, and occasional quiz nights.

LYMINGTON
BRASSERIE GERARD

MAP K (5)

113 High Street, Lymington, SO41 9AP
01590 688689 www.brasseriegerard.co.uk/location/lymington
SZ325955 50.7588, -1.5401
0900-2300 Mo-Sa; 0900-2230 Su.
None

This modern restaurant serves simple French cuisine all day. The interior is long and narrow, with a small bar and unostentatious décor. At the rear is a heated patio garden with plenty of seating. The brasserie's location on the handsome High Street, and the expanse of glazing on the street-facing side, make this a handy bolt hole in which to gain respite from, and to observe the bustle of, the Saturday market.

LYMINGTON
CHEQUERS INN

MAP K (6)

Ridgeway Lane, Lower Woodside, Lymington, SO41 8AH
01590 673415   www.chequersinnlymington.com
SZ322936   50.7416, -1.5449
1100-2300 Mo-Sa; 1200-2230 Su.

◖❱ S ✕ ᴥ ☻ ☂ ⛛ ❈ ⸻ ᴘ ⴕ P

Ringwood: Best Bitter, Fortyniner; occasional guests.

This pretty, ancient building on the edge of Lymington's salt marshes is handy for the nearby nature reserve and bracing coastal walks. The chequers sign memorializes the financial transactions of Lymington's defunct salt industry, whose exchequer offices were nearby. The open-plan interior, with exposed beams, log fire and dining area, is comfortable and relaxing. Outside are a large patio with a bar (summer only), and an attractive walled garden. The menu, from bar snacks to full restaurant meals, including fish and more exotic fare, is served all day.

LYMINGTON
FISHERMAN'S REST

MAP K (8)

All Saints Road, Woodside, Lymington, SO41 8FD
01590 678931   www.fullers.co.uk/rte.asp?id=4&itemid=106&task=View
SZ324946   50.7503, -1.5414
1130-2300 Mo-Sa; 1130-2230 Su.

◖❱ S ✕ ᴥ ☻ ☂ ❈ ⸻ ᴘ P ⊟

Fuller's: Gale's Seafarers Ale, London Pride, seasonals.

Originally a house named Grattens Cottage, granted a liquor licence in 1870, and a one-time smugglers' haunt, this old and traditional pub has open-plan lounge and restaurant areas around a central bar. The rustic, candlelit interior has exposed beams and an open fire; the walls are adorned with nauticalia, including local charts. Outside there is a small patio. The extensive menu includes local fish and seasonal produce. Thursday night is curry night. Among local attractions are Lymington's Saturday market, quay and marinas, sea wall walks and the marshes.

LYMINGTON AND PENNINGTON

LYMINGTON
FUSION INN

MAP K (10)

- Queen Street, Lymington, SO41 9NG
- 01590 672139
- SZ319954   50.7576, -1.5490
- 1100-1430, 1730-0100 Mo-Fr; 1100-0100 Sa; 1100-2230 Su.
- ◖▷ S ⛵ ♿ ❀ ⌇ ⛺ ⇌ ⊟

- Theakston: Best Bitter.

This late-Georgian building, with dentilled cornice, pilastered doorway and bay window, was once part of the estate of Devenish brewery (closed 1985). It is now a large and comfortable pub-cum-restaurant serving Thai food seven days a week, and hosting occasional sushi nights. Live music on one Friday evening per month is provided by acoustic guitar and piano. Televised sport is biased towards rugby.

LYMINGTON
GRAZE

MAP K (11)

- 9 Gosport Street, Lymington, SO41 9BG
- 01590 675595
- SZ326956   50.7594, -1.5383
- 1200-2400 Tu-Th; 1200-0100 Fr-Sa.
- ◖▷ ✗ ♞ ❀ ⇌ ⊟

- None

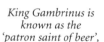

King Gambrinus is known as the 'patron saint of beer',

This bar-cum-restaurant, fronting onto a narrow pavement, has a handsome interior. Wood abounds from floor to ceiling; furnishing is modern, and includes seating and tables in booths. The menu is wide-ranging, and includes sharing platters. Fruits de mer is served but requires 24 hours' notice. The choice of drinks is oriented towards wines, spirits and cocktails, and there are cocktail promotions on Friday, which is also ladies' night. Parking is available in the council car park opposite.

LYMINGTON
HAVEN BAR & BISTRO

Lymington Yacht Haven, Kings Saltern Road, Lymington, SO41 3QD
01590 679971   www.havenrestaurant.co.uk
SZ332946   50.7506, - 1.5317
0900-2400.

◖▷ S ✗ ☙ ⛺ 🐕 ❀ ⸮ 𝌆 P

Ringwood: Best Bitter; occasional guests.

This modern bar and restaurant, popular with the sailing community, stands at the edge of the yacht haven and affords splendid views of the Solent and the Isle of Wight. Restaurant and snug are on the ground floor; the main bar is on the first floor, reached by stairs. There are separate menus for breakfast, lunch and dinner, and a varied fish menu. Rugby is the favoured televised sport.

LYMINGTON
KINGS ARMS

St Thomas Street, Lymington, SO41 9NB
01590 672594   www.kingsarmslymington.co.uk
SZ320953   50.7571, - 1.5476
1100-2300 Mo-Sa; 1200-2230 Su.

◖▷ S ☙ ⛺ 🐕 ♿ ✉ ❀ ⸮ 🎵 P ⇌ 🚌

Ringwood: Best Bitter.

This former coaching inn may date from the reign of Charles II. It stands near the western end of Lymington's main shopping street, at the outer reach of the busy Saturday market. The timber-framed first floor has a gabled projecting bay resting on carved lions. The interior is light and airy, furnished with comfortable chairs and settees; it hosts music events on Fridays and Saturdays (over 25s only). During winter, food is

served only on Saturday and Sunday lunchtimes. Nearby is St Thomas's church, a 13th century building restored in the 1700s.

LYMINGTON
KINGS HEAD INN

MAP K (15)

- ⌨ 1 Quay Hill, Lymington, SO41 3AR
- ☎ 01590 672709
- ↗ SZ326956   50.7591, -1.5381
- 🕐 1100-2400.

⟨▮ S ⭲ 🕴 ⛶ ⚏ ⇌ ⛆

🍺 Adnams: Broadside; Flack Manor: Double Drop; Fuller's: London Pride, Gale's HSB; Ringwood: Best Bitter.

The Kings Head is situated at the top of Quay Hill, a pedestrian street paved with setts and many of whose shops are Grade II listed. The bay-windowed façade advertises the split-level interior; the lower level appears to have originally housed a shop. Tankards hang from the beams within, and an open fire enhances the feeling of warmth in the woody interior. Food is served all day on Saturdays and Sundays. Follow the setts downhill to reach the quayside.

LYMINGTON
LANES OF LYMINGTON

MAP K (16)

- ⌨ Ashley Lane, High Street, Lymington, SO41 3RH
- ☎ 01590 672777   www.lanesoflymington.com
- ↗ SZ324955   50.7582, -1.5419
- 🕐 1130-1400, 1830-2400.

⟨▮ S ⭲ ♿ ⇌ ⛆

🍺 None

This bar and restaurant is in a converted 18th century church and school, a short walk from the High Street. Its interior is on several levels, light and airy, and with quiet furnishing and décor. Seasonal and local produce feature in the menus, which are divided into lunchtime and evening, bar and restaurant. Events include a monthly 'Party Night', with DJ and dancing, occasional live jazz, and cookery demonstrations. Nearby attractions include the High Street shops, Grove Gardens park and the Saturday market.

LYMINGTON
LONGS BAR

MAP K (17)

- 99 High Street , Lymington, SO41 9AP
- 01590 677550
- SZ324955   50.7585, -1.5413
- 2100-0200.
- ≥ 🚌
- None

St Arnold is the 'patron saint of brewing'.

The easy to miss entrance to this subterranean bar is adjacent to the Carphone Warehouse. The establishment attracts a young clientèle, and entertains them with an abundance of fruit machines, flashing lights, DJs, karaoke and occasional live music. Those wishing to enter after 10pm must pay an admission charge. Nearby attractions include the pubs, restaurants and shops of Lymington's High Street and environs.

LYMINGTON
MAYFLOWER

MAP K (18)

- Kings Saltern Road, Lymington, SO41 3QD
- 01590 672160   www.themayflower.uk.com
- SZ332950   50.7537, -1.5301
- 1100-2300 Mo-Sa; 1200-2200 Su.
- ◖❙ S ⛄ 🐾 ♿ 🍴 ❄ ⌐ ⚒ P ≥ 🚌
- Fuller's: London Pride; Goddards: Fuggle-Dee-Dum; Ringwood: Best Bitter; St Austell: Tribute; guests.
- Thatchers: Dry.

The Mayflower is a large pub with impressive chimneys and three bargeboarded gables atop protruding bays. The interior is divided into several areas, decorated in various shades of brown, and undeniably angular. Food is served all day, and includes daily specials and a children's menu; the pub also caters for functions. Children are not permitted in the bar after 7pm but may enjoy the large garden and its play area. There is live music weekly, and nearby attractions include the yacht haven and coastal walks.

NEW FOREST PUB GUIDE **73**

LYMINGTON
SHIP INN

- The Quay, Lymington, SO41 3AY
- 01590 676903   www.theshiplymington.co.uk
- SZ327956   50.7592, -1.5367
- 1100-2300.

Fuller's: London Pride; Wells and Young's: Young's Bitter; one guest.

An imposing presence on Lymington's quay, with dormers and a three-storey middle bay astride the entrance. The L-shaped interior includes quarry-tiled and stone floors, bare-brick walls and much wood; visitors in winter will benefit from a wood-burning fireplace of uncommon appearance. Outside there is a large, decked area overlooking the harbour. Food is served all day, and daily specials are augmented on Thursdays (grill night), Fridays (fish suppers) and Sundays (roasts); the children's menu emphasises 'real food'. Sailors may avail themselves of the showers.

LYMINGTON
THOMAS TRIPP

- Stanford Road, Lymington, SO41 9GF
- 01590 689047
- SZ319954   50.7576, -1.5492
- 1100-2300 Su-Th; 1100-0100 Fr-Sa.

Ringwood: Best Bitter, Fortyniner; occasional guests.

Named after a fictitious smuggler, the Thomas Tripp stands in an island formed by a one-way system. It was built in the 1700s, with two storeys and attic dormers, and has a lower, five-bay extension. There is a main bar, and a separate room which can be used for dining or functions. The pub specializes in fresh pizza and calzone, including takeaways, served most evenings and some lunchtimes. Lymington folk club meets here on Wednesday evenings, and there is also live music on Friday and Saturday evenings.

LYMINGTON
TOLLHOUSE INN

MAP K (23)

⌨ 167 Southampton Road, Lymington, SO41 9HA
☎ 01590 672142   www.tollhouseinn.co.uk
↗ SZ316964   50.7668, -1.5525
🕐 1100–2300 Mo–Sa; 1200–2230 Su.

◖❙ S ⛯ ⛺ ⛄ ♿ ☻ ⌐ ♫ P ♒

🍺 Ringwood: Best Bitter, Fortyniner; St Austell: Tribute.

A jumble of interconnected buildings forms the satisfyingly incoherent external view of the 18th century Tollhouse. Originally the Crown, later the Monkey House, it takes its current name from the turnpike tollhouse in the garden. The dining room has a low, beamed ceiling, and an open fire with bare brick surround. The elegant bar (which is open to the roof, whose supporting structure is nicely picked out) has wooden floors, wood-panelled walls, a fine fireplace, and comfortable seating. There is live music every weekend. Nearby is Buckland Rings Iron Age fort.

LYMINGTON
WISTARIA

MAP K (27)

⌨ 32 St Thomas Street, Lymington, SO41 9NE
☎ 01590 672078
↗ SZ320953   50.7572, -1.5474
🕐 1200–1430, 1900–2230 Tu–Th; 1200–1430, 1900–2300 Fr; 1100–2300 Sa; 1300–2230 Su.

◖ S ⛯ ⛺ ⛄ ♿ 🛏 ☻ P ⇌ ♒

🍺 Ringwood: Best Bitter.

Pedants should be aware that the spelling of the name of the American anatomist Caspar Wistar appears not to have been consistent. Notable external features of this handsome Georgian building include the door case, with pediment and pilasters, the dormers set behind a parapet, and the wisteria. The bar is light,

and simply-furnished; it offers snacks every lunchtime, meals on Thursday to Saturday lunchtimes, quiz or music nights on Friday, and bingo on Sunday evening. Accommodation is available in three en-suite rooms.

PENNINGTON
MUSKETEER

MAP K (19)

- 26 North Street, Pennington, SO41 8FZ
- 01590 676527
- SZ311949   50.7536, -1.5599
- 1130-1430, 1700-2330 Mo-Th; 1130-2400 Fr-Sa; 1200-2300 Su.

Ringwood: Best Bitter, Fortyniner; Wells and Young's: Courage Best; up to two guests.

Built in 1905 on the site of its burnt-down predecessor, and originally the Lion and Lamb, this pub has a lounge bar, with open fires and pew-like window seating, a family room, and a noteworthy inn sign. Home-cooked meals, soups and sandwiches are available lunch time and early evening. The adjacent building, with semi-circular windows, was built as a stable but never used as such. Regular events include monthly theme nights, live music on the first Saturday of the month. Tuesday is quiz night, and Thursday is 'curry and a pint' night.

PENNINGTON
WHITE HART

MAP K (26)

- 17 Milford Road, Pennington, SO41 8DF
- 01590 673495
- SZ316947   50.7517, -1.5524
- 1100-2300 Mo-Sa; 1200-2230 Su.

Ringwood: Best Bitter; up to two guests.

"They who drink beer will think beer."
WASHINGTON IRVING

This part tile-hung wayside inn, situated at busy Pennington Cross, was built in the late 1700s. The beamed interior has two bars; the main one serves a general seating area with panelled walls and an open fire, whilst the other serves the restaurant; between the two is a lounge area. Food, from snacks to meals, is served all day. Outside there is a covered patio and smoking area, and a large beer garden with a children's climbing frame. Entertainment includes a Monday night quiz and occasional live music.

76 NEW FOREST PUB GUIDE

BANK
OAK INN

MAP I (17)

- ⌨ Pinkney Lane, Bank, SO43 7FD
- ☎ 023 8028 2350   www.fullers.co.uk/rte.asp?id=243&itemid=190&task=View
- ↗ SU285071   50.8635, -1.5951
- ⏱ 1130-1500, 1800-2300 Mo-Fr; 1130-2300 Sa; 1200-2230 Su.

◖❙ S ⌖ ☕ ⛺ ♿ ⚙ ⌐ ⚒ P

- 🍺 Fuller's: Gale's Seafarers Ale, London Pride, Gale's HSB, seasonals; guests.

The Oak stands in a peaceful hamlet frequented by walkers, cyclists and ponies, a world apart from the nearby A35. Records of the building go back to the early 1700s. Its interior is low-beamed and abounding in wood. Also wooden are the cask-ends from which real ales are dispensed, propelled from the cellar by gas-driven pump. Food dominates (booking is recommended); specialities include game and seafood, and sandwiches are available at lunchtime. The K6 telephone box is both decorative and functional. No children aged under eight are allowed in the bar.

EMERY DOWN
NEW FOREST INN

MAP I (16)

- ⌨ Emery Down, SO43 7DY
- ☎ 023 8028 4690   www.thenewforestinn.co.uk
- ↗ SU285084   50.8744, -1.5955
- ⏱ 1130-2330 Mo-Th; 1130-0030 Fr-Sa; 1200-2300 Su.

◖❙ S ✗ ⌖ ☕ ♿ ⛉ ⚙ ⌐ ⚒ P

- 🍺 Ringwood: Best Bitter, Fortyniner; guests.
- 🍎 Occasional guests.

This sprawling building in an attractive village is said to have originated as a gypsy caravan and thence to have grown; the spacious interior is on several levels, and the delightful, wooded garden on several more. Food is served all day, includes vegetarian and vegan options, and favours locally-sourced produce. There is a quiz night on the last Tuesday of the month, and a beer and music festival in July. Four letting rooms provide a good base for exploration, including a visit to the nearby Portuguese Fireplace.

EMERY DOWN
SWAN INN

MAP I (22)

✉ Swan Green, Emery Down, SO43 7DT
☎ 023 8028 2203   www.theswanlyndhurst.co.uk
↗ SU290081   50.8722, -1.5881
🕐 1000-2300 Mo-Sa; 1000-2230 Su.

🍺 Ringwood: Best Bitter, Fortyniner; guests.

The handsome Swan Inn stands opposite the cricket ground and the much photographed thatched cottages of Swan Green. It was built in 1731 as a coaching inn, complete with blacksmith's forge, and underwent a major rebuild following a disastrous fire in 2006. The large interior has separate bar and dining areas, and there is a children's play area in the garden. Food is served all day, and the pub is a popular rendezvous for walkers seeking refreshment. There are three letting rooms.

LYNDHURST
COBURNS

MAP I (3)

✉ 24 High Street, Lyndhurst, SO43 7BG
☎ 023 8028 4480
↗ SU299082   50.8725, -1.5761
🕐 1830-2300 We; 1830-2400 Th-Sa; 1830-2230 Su.

🍺 None.

Although Coburns does not serve draught real ale, it stocks a number of bottled beers, usually from the Oakleaf and Ringwood breweries. The entrance to this bistro bar has a handsome, pedimented door case; on offer within is a good choice of meals, snacks and wines. The bar is on the ground floor; ascent to additional seating on the first floor is via a spiral staircase. A ramp is available to facilitate wheelchair access to the main bar.

LYNDHURST
CROWN HOTEL

MAP I (4)

🖂 9 High Street, Lyndhurst, SO43 7NF
☎ 023 8028 2922   www.crownhotel-lyndhurst.co.uk
↗ SU298082   50.8726, -1.5779
🕐 1000-2300.

◖❱ S ➳ ☆ ♿ 🛏 ❀ ⚓ 🎦 P 🚌

🍺 Ringwood: Best Bitter.

This 38 bedroom hotel stands close to but aloof from Lyndhurst's main street. It was built in 1896 on the site of the Crown Inn; Norman Shaw influenced, with half-timbered gables, stone dressing, much tile-hanging, and a timber arch over the carriageway entrance. The hotel serves unpretentious, locally-sourced food, and entertains with live jazz on the third Sunday afternoon of the month. At the rear are a patio and a fine garden. In the churchyard opposite is the grave of Alice Hargreaves, née Liddell (ask any Lewis Carroll fan).

LYNDHURST
CROWN STIRRUP

MAP I (5)

🖂 12 Clay Hill, Lyndhurst, SO43 7DE
☎ 023 8028 2339   www.crownstirrup.com
↗ SU301070   50.8620, -1.5725
🕐 1200-2300.

◖❱ S ➳ ☆ ❀ ⚓ 🎦 🅰 P 🚌

🍺 Ringwood: Best Bitter, Fortyniner; one guest.
🍏 New Forest: at least one cider.

"I drink therefore I am."
WC FIELDS

Part of the building dates from the 1400s, some of the beams came from Bucklers Hard, and the name refers to the size limit for commoners' hunting dogs. The interior is a homely, single space, part quarry-tiled, and with exposed brickwork and a wood-panelled dado; furniture includes leather armchairs and sofa. The large garden has a children's play area, a fire pit (lit at weekends) and a bar (summer only). Food (cassoulet a speciality) is served all day, and walkers may avail themselves of the takeaway service. Live music on Fridays.

LYNDHURST
FOREST LODGE HOTEL

MAP I (8)

Pikes Hill, Lyndhurst, SO43 7AS
023 8028 3677 www.newforesthotels.co.uk/hotels/forest-lodge-hotel-lyndhurst
SU297086 50.8767, -1.5779
1100-2300.
None

This 3* hotel with 38 bedrooms stands at the northwestern edge of the town, close to the police headquarters. It has been extensively refurbished in recent years, and offers excellent accommodation to holiday and business visitors. The chic bar area, with modern décor, offers a range of light meals and bar snacks from midday until 2pm and 6pm until 9pm; the restaurant is for residents only. Outside seating is provided on the decked terrace at the front of the hotel.

LYNDHURST
FOX & HOUNDS

MAP I (10)

22 High Street, Lyndhurst, SO43 7BG
023 8028 2098 www.foxandhoundslyndhurst.co.uk
SU299082 50.8725, -1.5763
1100-2300 Mo-Sa; 1200-2230 Su.
Fuller's: Gale's HSB; Ringwood: Best Bitter, Fortyniner; St Austell: Tribute.

The Fox & Hounds is a large Georgian pub of invitingly irregular appearance. It was built in two parts and altered in subsequent centuries; its entrance is in a half-hexagonal wing. The interior has antique furniture and many exposed beams. Food on offer is from standard lunchtime and evening menus, and is supplemented with daily specials. Dogs and smokers are welcome in the garden. Events include a quiz on Monday, and live music on Fridays. The pub is close to the New Forest Museum.

LYNDHURST
LA PERGOLA

MAP I (11)

⊟ Southampton Road, Lyndhurst, SO43 7BQ
℗ 023 8028 4184   www.la-pergola.co.uk
↗ SU304082   50.8730, -1.5691
🕑 1100-1430, 1800-2300 Tu-Su.

◖▶ 🐴 ♿ 🍽 ☕ P 🚍

🍺 None

An Italian restaurant and wine bar fronted, perhaps unsurprisingly, by a very large pergola. This attractive building saw service as tea rooms and as a pub before acquiring its current identity. The interior is light, airy and peaceful; the garden offers relaxation for adults and excitement for children. Opposite is Bolton's Bench, named after the Duke of Bolton; it is a spot long favoured by picnickers, ponies and the studiously idle; near the Bench is a cricket pitch.

LYNDHURST
LYNDHURST PARK HOTEL

MAP I (13)

⊟ High Street, Lyndhurst, SO43 7NL
℗ 023 8028 3923   www.lyndhurstparkhotel.co.uk
↗ SU302081   50.8722, -1.5714
🕑 1200-2300.

◖▶ S ✗ 🐴 🛏 ♿ 🛌 ☕ P 🚍

🍺 Ringwood: Best Bitter.

The Lyndhurst Park guards the entrance to five acres of grounds at the eastern end of the town centre. There is a wood panelled bar serving a seating area which has modern décor and sports television; both the bar and the adjacent cosy lounge overlook the picturesque gardens. Light meals and snacks are served in the bar; English and Continental cuisine is served in the grand, oak-panelled Tudor Restaurant, adjacent to which is the Palm Room conservatory.

LYNDHURST
MAILMANS ARMS

MAP I (14)

71 High Street, Lyndhurst, SO43 7BE
023 8028 4196   www.mailmans-arms.co.uk
SU300082   50.8726, -1.5741
1100-2300.

◖◗ S 🐕 🐎 🛋 ❀ ⌐ ⚒ P 🚗

Greene King: IPA, Abbot Ale; one guest.

The elegant façade of this pub has a part-timbered gable above an oriel with herringbone brickwork, and in summer it is adorned with flowers. The interior is open-plan, simply furnished and with stained glass lampshades above the bar; reminders of the former two-bar layout survive on the etched front windows. Outdoor seating is provided on the street-facing patio and in the rear garden. Occasional events include hog-roasts, barbecues, discos and quizzes. Those with an embarrassment of loose change may wish to explore the neighbouring Maserati and Ferrari showroom.

LYNDHURST
MILL

MAP I (15)

Romsey Road, Lyndhurst, SO43 7AR
023 8028 2814
SU298085   50.8755, -1.5768
1100-2300 Mo-Sa; 1200-2300 Su.

◖◗ S ✕ 🐕 ♿ 🛋 ❀ ⌐ ⚓ P 🚗

Summer only – Greene King: IPA; Shepherd Neame: Spitfire.

This large former guesthouse, just north of Lyndhurst town centre, is now a pub / restaurant with nine letting rooms. The interior has a large, U-shaped bar, seating on various levels, and entertainment in the forms of a children's ball-pit, a pool table and television. Outside are numerous benches on both the patio and the grassed area. Food is served all day, and in summer there are occasional family fun-days. Budding card sharks should mosey along to the Sunday evening poker tables (entry fee applies).

LYNDHURST
STAG HOTEL

MAP I (21)

🖃 69 High Street, Lyndhurst, SO43 7BE
① 023 8028 2999   www.stag-hotel.co.uk
↗ SU300082   50.8726, -1.5743
🕐 1100-2300.

◖❱ ✖ ➤ ♞ ⇔ ⊛ ⌐ ⚊ ⚌ P 🚃

🍺 Greene King: IPA.

*"Beer is proof that God
loves us and wants us to
be happy."*
BENJAMIN FRANKLIN

The rumbustiously handsome Stag Hotel bears the date 1907 on the leadwork beneath an oriel, and on the keystone of the arch above its main entrance; its corner entrance is beneath a two-storey oriel tower. The elegant bar is carpeted and dadoed, and has leather seating; the restaurant 'El Bosque' is a tapas bar and brasserie which offers a carvery menu on Sundays. There is a large patio and decking area to the rear, with a covered area for smokers. Accommodation is in 11 en-suite rooms.

LYNDHURST
WATERLOO ARMS

MAP I (23)

🖃 Pikes Hill, Lyndhurst, SO43 7AS
① 023 8028 2113   www.waterlooarmsnewforest.co.uk
↗ SU297087   50.8775, -1.5790
🕐 1130-2300 Mo-Sa; 1130-2230 Su.

◖❱ S ✖ ➤ ♞ & ⊛ ⌐ ⚊ ⚌ ⚱ P 🚃

🍺 Ringwood: Best Bitter,Fortyniner; Sharp's: Doom Bar.
🍎 Thatchers: Traditional.

The Waterloo Arms is a thatched pub situated at the northern edge of Lyndhurst, close to the source of the Beaulieu River and handy for the police headquarters. The interior is low-beamed, with bare-brick and wood-panelling; furniture includes leather sofas, and décor includes farm implements. To the rear is a fenced and well-maintained garden. Food is served all day on Saturday

and Sunday, and the regular menu is supplemented by specials which may from time to time include exotic meats (wildebeest anybody?).

MARCHWOOD
PILGRIM INN

MAP E (11)

✉ Hythe Road, Marchwood, SO40 4WU
☎ 023 8086 7752   www.fullers.co.uk/rte.asp?id=243&itemid=368&task=View
↗ SU387096   50.8848, -1.4506
🕐 1100-2300 Mo-Sa; 1200-2230 Su.

◖◗ S ✕ ⛖ 🛏 & ⛟ ✿ ♨ P ⛴

🍺 Fuller's: Chiswick Bitter, London Pride, Gale's HSB, ESB; one seasonal.

Built as two thatched cottages in the 1700s, and much extended, the Pilgrim stands in attractive gardens between the Totton to Fawley railway line (goods only) and the Marchwood bypass. There are two attractive, thatched buildings: one houses the bedrooms; the other the pub and restaurant, with beams, exposed brickwork, and a handsome fireplace. Breakfast, lunch and dinner are served, and the wide-ranging menu includes *New Forest Marque* produce. The New Forest Wildlife Park is three miles to the west.

MARCHWOOD
ROEBUCK

MAP E (13)

✉ Main Road, Marchwood, SO40 4SF
☎ 023 8066 3036   www.theroebuckinnmarchwood.co.uk
↗ SU386102   50.8905, -1.4514
🕐 1200-2300 Mo-Th; 1200-2400 Fr-Sa; 1200-2230 Su.

◖◗ S ⛖ 🛏 & ⛟ ✿ ⅃ P ⛴

🍺 Ringwood: Best Bitter.

The Roebuck, built in the 1980s, is situated in a small shopping precinct. An S-shaped bar stands to one side of a large room that also houses a stage, a pool table and televisions for the screening of sporting events, and which occasionally hosts quiz nights. Food, consisting of traditional pub fare, is served all day. There are five en-suite guest rooms, but note that breakfast is not provided. Both The New Forest Wildlife Park and Longdown Activity Farm are to the west and within three miles.

MARCHWOOD
WHITE HORSE

MAP E (19)

- ⌧ Main Road, Marchwood, SO40 4US
- ☎ 023 8066 3077
- ↗ SU389104   50.8923, -1.4478
- ◷ 1100-2300 Mo-Th; 1100-2400 Fr-Sa; 1200-2230 Su.

◖♪ S ⛵ 🍴 🛏 🐾 🍽 ⌂ 🎵 P 🚌

🛏 Two guests.

The building is Georgian, altered and extended, and was once a bakery; it is now a single-bar pub, converted from a two-bar configuration. The bar has original beams, two real fires, a pool table and sports television. Food consists of reasonably-priced, home-cooked pub fare, and there is a children's menu. The White Horse presents monthly live music, and hosts a quiz night every Sunday. Upstairs are three bedrooms with a shared lounge and kitchen, available for overnight stays or longer lets.

KEYHAVEN
GUN INN

MAP L (4)

- Keyhaven Road, Keyhaven, SO41 0TP
- 01590 642391   www.theguninn.com
- SZ305914   50.7222, -1.5683
- 1100-1500, 1800-2300 Mo-Fr; 1100-2300 Sa; 1200-1700 Su.

- Greene King: Old Speckled Hen; Ringwood: Best Bitter; Sharp's: Doom Bar; Timothy Taylor: Landlord.
- Westons: Old Rosie.

This 18th century pub was named after Colonel Hawker's punt gun. There is a cosy bar with beamed ceiling, family rooms with interesting antiques, and a summer bar in the large garden. Food includes daily specials and fresh crab; malt whiskies number over 200. Bar billiards can be played here. Parking is available in the public facility opposite (charges may apply). A seasonal ferry runs from the nearby quay to Henry VIII's Hurst Castle and to Yarmouth, and the Solent Way passes the front door. Hurst Beach and the marshes offer bracing walks and ornithological interest.

MILFORD-ON-SEA
BELLE EPOQUE

MAP L (2)

- 11 High Street, Milford-on-Sea, SO41 0QF
- 01590 645300
- SZ289918   50.7255, -1.5908
- 1000-2200 We-Su.

- None

Cenosillicaphobia is fear of an empty glass.

A former antique shop, now an uncommon mix of off-licence, bar, café, restaurant, second-hand bookshop and bric-à-brac store. Newspapers and magazines are available to read, books may be purchased, and food and drink may be enjoyed. Varied meals, snacks and platters are offered throughout the day, with more formal meals available in the evening. Bottle-conditioned beers may sometimes be available.

MILFORD-ON-SEA
MARINE   MAP L (6)

- Hurst Road, Milford-on-Sea, SO41 0PY
- 01590 644369   www.themarinerestaurant.co.uk
- SZ294911   50.7193, -1.5840
- 1000-1600 Mo-We; 1000-1600, 1800-2200 Th-Fr; 0930-1600, 1800-2200 Sa; 0930-1600 Su.

◖◗ S ✕ ➹ 🐴 ♿ ❀ ⚓ P ☕

- Two guests.

This Art Deco establishment, dramatically situated at the landward end of Hurst Beach, opened in 2010, replacing an Art Deco beach café. Breathtaking views of the Solent, the Needles and Christchurch Bay may be enjoyed from its ground floor café-bar and patio, first floor restaurant and balcony, and roof terrace; dogs are welcome on the patio. The innovative menu features locally-sourced ingredients, and events include tapas nights and occasional acoustic music. The Marine is adjacent to Sturt Pond Nature Reserve, and a rewarding 1½ mile walk from Hurst Castle.

MILFORD-ON-SEA
RED LION   MAP L (9)

- 32 High Street, Milford-on-Sea, SO41 0QD
- 01590 642236   www.redlionpubmilfordonsea.co.uk
- SZ290918   50.7256, -1.5903
- 1130-1430, 1800-2300 Mo-Sa; 1200-1530 Su.

◖◗ S ➹ 🐴 ♿ 🛏 ❀ ⚑ ⚓ P ☕

- Fuller's: London Pride; Ringwood: Best Bitter; one guest.
- Broadoak: Moonshine.

Built as a Georgian coaching inn, the pub was later extended into the former stables and hayloft; the three buildings form a handsome group whose front entrance has a porch with Doric pillars. The large bar is on several levels, and has a central open fireplace; part of the area is reserved for pool and darts players. The three en-suite rooms face the large, lawned garden to the rear of the pub. Food is home-cooked; live music is monthly; Milford beach is 700 yards away.

MILFORD-ON-SEA
SMUGGLERS INN

MAP L (11)

- 88 High Street, Milford-on-Sea, SO41 0QE
- 01590 644414   www.pubsnewforest.co.uk/?page_id=10
- SZ291918   50.7253, -1.5880
- 1100-2300 Mo-Sa; 1200-2230 Su.

◖▮ S ✕ ⛵ ♿ ☕ ⊷ ⚒ Å P ⛟

Greene King: Abbot Ale; Ringwood: Best Bitter; Timothy Taylor: Landlord.

Originally the Crown Inn, built in 1803, this former coaching inn has rendered walls, sash windows and a tiled roof. The door has a reeded frame and flat hood supported on scrolled brackets. Timbers from old barns were used to construct the beamed ceilings of its spacious and handsome interior, which has a separate bar and restaurant. Food features locally-sourced ingredients; 90% of the meat comes from Hampshire. There is occasional live music linked to special events such as Milford Food Week in April. The beach is but 600 yards away.

MILFORD-ON-SEA
WHITE HORSE

MAP L (15)

- 16 Keyhaven Road, Milford-on-Sea, SO41 0QY
- 01590 642360
- SZ293917   50.7247, -1.5862
- 1100-1500, 1700-2300 Mo-Sa; 1200-1500, 1800-2230 Su.

◖▮ S ⛵ ♿ ☕ Å P ⛟

Ringwood: Best Bitter, Fortyniner; Sharp's: Doom Bar; two guests.

Said to have been built in the 18th century, the White Horse may incorporate the Kings Arms which stood on the site in 1720. Entry from the car park is via an extensive garden. The single, L-shaped bar has small alcoves furnished with bench seating. The long-established menu features home-made fare; specialities include the pie of the day and Great British Puddings, and there are regular curry nights. Live music is occasionally presented. It is a ½ mile to the beach, and one mile to the delights of Keyhaven and the marshes.

CANTERTON
SIR WALTER TYRRELL

MAP C (8)

- ✉ Canterton Lane, Canterton, SO43 7HD
- ☎ 023 8081 3170   www.sirwaltertyrrell.co.uk
- ↗ SU268127   50.9131, -1.6191
- 🕐 1100–2300 Mo–Sa; 1100–2230 Su.

◖❙ S ☎ 🍴 ♿ ❀ 🎵 🛠 P

🍺 Ringwood: Best Bitter, Fortyniner; two guests.

This large pub was built in the 1930s. Its name is that of the man whose arrow killed William II (William Rufus) in 1100, at a supposed location marked by the nearby Rufus Stone. The comfortable interior is reminiscent of the grander roadhouse style 1960s pub, wood-panelled and with a brick fireplace. Food is served all day, and there is a separate menu for children who, once replete, may enjoy the adventure playground. The brick-built house in the top car park was once a pub called The Stump, after its one-legged landlady.

MINSTEAD
TRUSTY SERVANT

MAP C (9)

- ✉ Minstead, SO43 7FY
- ☎ 023 8081 2137
- ↗ SU281110   50.8982, -1.6011
- 🕐 1100–2300 (summer); 1100–1500, 1800–2300 Mo–We; 1100–2300 Th–Su (winter).

◖❙ S ✕ ☎ 🍴 ❀ ⌐ 🛠 P

🍺 Adnams: Southwold Bitter; Fuller's: Gale's HSB; Ringwood: Best Bitter.

This Victorian pub, built by Winchester College, stands by Minstead's village green, close to the delightful All Saints Church, burial place of Sir Arthur Conan Doyle. The eponymous servant is the composite beast depicted on the inn sign, which is a copy of a painting in the College. The bar and dining area are wood-floored, decorated in modern style, and warmed by four wood-burning fires. Food is available all day at weekends. To the rear are a patio and a large garden. Furzey Gardens is a mile away.

NETLEY MARSH
WHITE HORSE

MAP D (14)

⌨ Ringwood Road, Netley Marsh, SO40 7GX
☎ 023 8086 2166   www.whitehorsenetleymarsh.co.uk
↗ SU332129   50.9151, -1.5290
🕐 1130-2300.

◖ S ✕ ⛔ ♞ ⚙ ⌣ Ⓐ P 🚊

🍺 Ringwood: Best Bitter, Fortyniner; one guest.
🍎 Westons: Old Rosie; one guest.

A traditional local whose beamed interior has an L-shaped bar serving the main seating area, and a stone-floored public bar with darts and table football. Televised sport also features. The pub favours local produce, which includes meat from a nearby farm, and bottled ciders from Mr Whitehead's and the New Forest cider companies. Outside seating is available on the patio at the front and side of the pub. No food is served on Monday evenings. Quiz night is on Sunday and there is live music every Friday night.

WOODLANDS
GAMEKEEPER

MAP D (5)

⌨ 268 Woodlands Road, Woodlands, SO40 7GH
☎ 023 8029 3093   www.thegamekeeperpub.co.uk
↗ SU325119   50.9057, -1.5392
🕐 1100-2300.

◖ S ✕ ⛔ ♞ ♿ ⚙ ⌣ ♒ P 🚊

🍺 Wadworth: Henry's IPA, 6X; two guests.
🍎 Westons: Old Rosie.

Built over 100 years ago, the former Royal Oak is a cosy community pub whose interior features exposed beams and a wood-burning stove. There are separate areas for drinkers and diners, the former with a dart board and television. Outdoor seating is provided on the rear patio and in the long, narrow garden, which has a children's play area.

Food is served all day, and includes specials and a children's menu. On Friday nights there is live music. Henry's IPA is sold as Gamekeeper Poachers Ale.

ASHLEY
ASHLEY

MAP L (1)

- Ashley Road, Ashley, BH25 5BP
- 01425 612277
- SZ255953   50.7574, -1.6395
- 1400-2330 Mo-Th; 1200-2330 Fr-Sa; 1100-2330 Su.

One occasional guest.

Formerly the Ashley Hotel, now simply the Ashley, this pub's single, large bar puts the emphasis on sport. There are two pool tables, table football, and a sports television with a projector screen. Pool is free on Mondays, Wednesdays and Fridays, and there is a poker tournament on Tuesdays. The garden has a children's play area. Simple pub fare is served at weekend lunchtimes, and musical entertainment is provided by a disco or a live band on either Friday or Saturday night.

ASHLEY
OAK & YAFFLE

MAP H (7)

- Ashley Common Road, Ashley, BH25 5AN
- 01425 618276
- SZ250962   50.7650, -1.6456
- 1600-2300 Mo-Fr; 1200-2300 Sa; 1200-2230 Su.

Ringwood: Fortyniner.

A large, post-war pub with an enormous car park, the Oak and Yaffle has two public rooms: the public bar offers darts and television; the restaurant offers English and Thai food between 6pm and 9pm daily, and additionally between midday and 2pm on Saturday and Sunday. Further exoticism is provided by Wednesday's curry night. The small garden leading off the public bar is furnished with benches. Yaffle is an old name for the green woodpecker; the word is onomatopoeic.

BARTON-ON-SEA
CLIFF HOUSE HOTEL

MAP H (3)

- Marine Drive West, Barton-on-Sea, BH25 7QL
- 01425 619333   www.thecliffhouse.co.uk
- SZ232931   50.7371, -1.6714
- 1000-2200 Mo-Sa; 1000-1600 Su.

◖▮ S ✕ ⛴ ⌂ ❀ P ⊟

- None

A restaurant and hotel with seven bedrooms, whose light and airy bar is open to those wanting only a drink, as is the patio, which has a real fire. This welcoming establishment is situated on a cliff top, and affords magnificent views across Christchurch Bay to Purbeck, and across the Solent to the Isle of Wight. Food is not served on Sunday evening and Monday. Wheelchair access is possible but there are no special adaptations.

BARTON-ON-SEA
HOUSE MARTIN

MAP H (5)

- Christchurch Road, Barton-on-Sea, BH25 6QF
- 01425 618521
- SZ232940   50.7451, -1.6725
- 1100-2300 Mo-Sa; 1200-2230 Su.

◖▮ S ✕ ⛴ ✝ ⛓ ❀ ⚏ P ⊟

- Hall & Woodhouse: Badger First Gold, Tanglefoot, seasonals.

This traditional, large, suburban pub, set back a little from the road and near the recreation ground, puts the accent on food, which is available all day. 'The Barn' is the main dining area; it has an open fire and is available for functions. Dogs are welcome only in the bar. New Milton station and the coast are less than a mile away (in different directions).

NEW MILTON

BARTON-ON-SEA
PEBBLE BEACH

MAP H (8)

- ✉ Marine Drive, Barton-on-Sea, BH25 7DZ
- ☎ 01425 627777   www.pebblebeach-uk.com
- ↗ SZ238929   50.7361, -1.6639
- 🕐 1100-1430, 1800-2300 Mo-Fr; 1100-1500, 1800-2300 Sa; 1200-1500, 1830-2230 Su.

◖❯ S ✕ 🛥 ♿ 🛏 ❀ P 🚌

- 🍺 None

A *Michelin* and *Good Food Guide* listed restaurant situated on the cliff top, and with a veranda affording views across the waters to the Isle of Wight and Purbeck. It has three bedrooms and a penthouse; the latter is available for functions. The kitchen produces a seasonally changing menu offering a range of dishes that cater for all tastes from light lunches to formal dinners. Ringwood Fortyniner is available in bottles.

NEW MILTON
CHEWTON GLEN HOTEL

MAP H (2)

- ✉ Christchurch Road, New Milton, BH25 6QS
- ☎ 01425 275341   www.chewtonglen.com
- ↗ SZ225940   50.7456, -1.6813
- 🕐 1100-2400.

◖❯ ✕ 🛥 ♿ 🛏 ❀ ⌁ 🏊 P 🚌

- 🍺 None

This luxury country house hotel and spa is set in 130 acres of countryside; Walkford Brook runs through the grounds. Snacks are often available but the needs of residents take priority. The hamlet of Chewton can be traced back to the Normans, but the earliest part of the current building is probably

Georgian. Captain Frederick Marryat lived here in the 1840s while he gathered material for his novel, *The Children of the New Forest*; many of the rooms in the hotel are named after his novels.

NEW MILTON
MILTON BARNS

MAP H (6)

Gore Road, New Milton, BH25 6SJ
01425 618800   www.miltonbarns.co.uk
SZ234947   50.7515, -1.6689
0900-1800 winter; extended evening opening during summer.

None

Originally part of Gore Farm, this two-storey, Grade II listed building is a superb conversion of a former barn, with much wood and exposed brick, and spectacular exposed beams, purlins and rafters. Furniture is modern and elegant. There is an interesting menu, accommodation in 10 bedrooms, and a conservatory which is available for functions. The large adventure playground behind the restaurant is not part of the business but may nonetheless be enjoyed by children. Free Wi-Fi is available on request.

NEW MILTON
RYDAL ARMS

MAP H (10)

93 Station Road, New Milton, BH25 6JJ
01425 610619
SZ245946   50.7512, -1.6540
1100-2300 Mo-We; 1100-2400 Th-Sa; 1200-2300 Su.

Ringwood: Best Bitter; Sharp's: Doom Bar; Wychwood: Hobgoblin.

Once the domain of the UK's longest-serving landlady (1951-2001), the Rydal Arms is a handsome pub with a fine bow window, and a tree-bordered garden with a children's play area. The interior is adorned with pictures and artefacts, and warmed by three real fires. At the rear is a separate stage area, with projector screen and enormous glitter ball, which hosts live bands on Thursdays and

Saturdays, and a disco on Friday. Food is available all day at weekends. Children are permitted in the pub until 9pm every day.

NEW MILTON
WELLINGTONS

MAP H (11)

- ⌨ 2–4 Osborne Road, New Milton, BH25 6AD
- ☎ 01425 618464
- ↗ SZ243951   50.7554, –1.6559
- 🕐 1100–2300 Mo–Sa; 1200–2230 Su.

S 🐴 🏇 🐕 ♿ ⚰ 👪 ⛟ ⇌ 🚌

- 🍺 Wells and Young's: Courage Directors.

The building housing the former
Wellington Brasserie, close to New
Milton rail station, was created from the
conjunction of two terraced houses. The
interior is divided into a bar, with much
brickwork on view, and a cosy and
comfortably furnished lounge.
Entertainment includes pool, darts and
television, and there is live music on
Saturday evenings. The food offering
leans towards sandwiches and variations on a theme of burger and chips.

NEW MILTON
WHEATSHEAF

MAP H (12)

- ⌨ Christchurch Road, New Milton, BH25 6QJ
- ☎ 01425 611082
- ↗ SZ237942   50.7475, –1.6642
- 🕐 1100–2300 Mo–Th; 1100–2400 Fr; 1100–2300 Sa; 1130–2300 Su.

◐ ▶ S ✗ 🐴 🏇 🐕 🐾 ♿ ⚰ 👪 P ⇌ 🚌

- 🍺 Ringwood: Best Bitter, Fortyniner; two guests from Marston's Beer Company.

This traditional town pub dating back over 200 years is in the centre of Old
Milton, immediately opposite Old Milton Green. New Milton station is
just over ½ mile away and the coast is less than a mile away. The large

restaurant offers a
carvery, grill and salad
bar. There is a quiz on
Wednesdays, a folk
club on Thursdays and
a live band on Fridays.
The large television in
the bar shows sport.
The pleasant garden is
hidden from the road
and includes a
barbecue.

WOOTTON
RISING SUN

MAP H (9)

Bashley Common Road, Wootton, BH25 5SF
01425 610360   www.therisingsunbashley.co.uk
SZ242983   50.7845, –1.6572
1100–2300 Mo–Sa; 1200–2230 Su.

Fuller's: Gale's HSB; Ringwood: Best Bitter; Wells and Young's: Wells
Bombardier; one guest.

Thatchers: Traditional.

A handsome, Victorian building, with an impressive gable and unusually large pairs of eyebrowed windows. It looks out onto New Forest greens where ponies roam. Entry is through doors whose stained glass depicts the name of the pub; the interior is divided into numerous areas, including a restaurant, and has two open fires. Outside is a large garden, with patio, and a children's play area. The extensive menu caters for all tastes, and there are daily specials. Close to Bashley Park and an extensive campsite.

VERDERERS AND AGISTERS

The authority over Forest bye-laws and Commoners' Rights rests in the hands of the Verderers' Court, a body that can trace its history back almost a thousand years to the Conquest but which was redefined in 1877 by the Great New Forest Act of that year. The Court sits monthly, at the Queen's House in Lyndhurst, is open to the public and operates much like a magistrates' court.

There are ten Verderers. The Head Verderer is appointed by the Queen, and there are five elected members and four more appointed by the Forestry Commission, DEFRA, Natural England and the National Park.

The Court employs five Agisters to do its bidding. They keep an eye on stock conditions, ensuring that Commoners are looking to the welfare of their animals, paying their marking fees and keeping to the bye-laws. They also organize the annual pony round-ups ('drifts') but sadly their main duty in modern times is attending road accidents involving the Forest's animal population.

HAMPTWORTH
CUCKOO INN

MAP C (3)

- ⌨ Hamptworth Road, Hamptworth, SP5 2DU
- ☎ 01794 390302
- ↗ SU243196　　　　50.9757, -1.6543
- 🕐 1200-2300 Mo-Fr; 1130-2300 Sa; 1200-2300 Su.
  ◖ S 🐂 ♿ 🕷 ⌐ 🛏 P

- 🍺 Bowman: Elderado; Hop Back: GFB, Summer Lightning; Ringwood: Best Bitter; guests.
- 🍎 Frams.

A small, four-roomed, beautiful and endearingly quirky thatched pub serving beer drawn direct from casks in the ground floor cellar. Lunchtime food is served (snacks only on Monday and Tuesday), and on Friday evenings a fish and chip van visits. Indoor games include darts and cribbage; outside are a pétanque terrain for the active, and an adults-only area for the contemplative. A beer and music festival is held in late summer. Elderado and GFB are sold as Cuckoorado and Old School respectively; other beers may also have house names.

NOMANSLAND
LAMB INN

MAP C (5)

- ⌨ Forest Road, Nomansland, SP5 2BP
- ☎ 01794 390246　　www.the-lamb-inn-nomansland.co.uk
- ↗ SU253173　　　　50.9547, -1.6408
- 🕐 1100-1500, 1800-2300 Mo-Th; 1100-2300 Fr-Sa; 1200-2230 Su.
  ◖ ▶ S ✗ 🐂 🛏 🕷 ⌐ 🛏 ▲ P 🚌

- 🍺 Fuller's: Gale's HSB; Sharp's: Doom Bar; Timothy Taylor: Landlord; one guest.

The border separating Hampshire and Wiltshire used to pass through the Lamb; these days Hampshire must be satisfied with a few steps. The pub overlooks the village cricket field and a well-grazed green, beyond which are beech woods. Inside are a bar and restaurant, and a games area with a pool table towards the rear of the bar; beyond that is a lovely beer garden which blazes with colour during summer. There is an extensive choice of food, participation in the consumption of which is the condition for children's entry.

REDLYNCH
KINGS HEAD

MAP P (1)

The Row, Redlynch, SP5 2JT
01725 510240
SU201212 50.9902, -1.7139
1200-1500, 1800-2300 Mo; 1100-1500, 1800-2300 Tu-Th; 1100-1500, 1800-2400 Fr-Sa; 1200-1500, 1900-2300 Su.
P
Hop Back: Summer Lightning; Ringwood: Best Bitter.

This 18th century building, a one-time cider house, stands next to the erstwhile Southampton to Salisbury road. Its single bar has original beams decorated with brass ornaments, and is divided into several discrete areas; outside is a garden with benches and seats. The varied and continually changing menu offers locally-sourced, freshly-cooked food, including 'lunch in a loaf', and the pub holds several food festivals (such as pie, pasty and sausage) and an annual cider festival. Quiz night is every third Thursday, and there is live music at least once per month.

POULNER
LONDON TAVERN

MAP F (9)

⌨ Linford Road, Poulner, BH24 1TY
☎ 01425 473819   www.thelondontavern.co.uk
↗ SU163061   50.8543, -1.7689
🕐 1130-2330 Mo-Sa; 1200-2300 Su.

◖) S ✕ ☞ ☙ ☕ ♨ P ⊟

🍺 Ringwood: Best Bitter, Fortyniner; Timothy Taylor: Landlord; one guest.

The story begins in the 1860s. Johnny Londoner was the nickname of John Roberts, a man so outraged by the refusal of the White Hart's landlord to supply medicinal brandy that he opened a bar in his own house. It is a handsome building, brick-built and diamond patterned; its large bar with an open fireplace, and a separate dining room. Food, much of which is locally-sourced, is available all day. There are weekly music events and quiz nights, and the pub is close to Blashford Lakes nature reserve.

POULNER
WHITE HART INN

MAP F (15)

⌨ 171 Southampton Road, Poulner, BH24 1HU
☎ 01425 483123
↗ SU161058   50.8519, -1.7721
🕐 1200-2330.

◖) S ✕ ☞ ☙ ☕ ⌂ ♨ P ⊟

🍺 Ringwood: Best Bitter, Fortyniner; one guest.

The White Hart, situated on what was once a main road, is an 18th century inn, low-ceilinged and full of character. Within are three rooms: the public bar has a pool table and dart board; the cosy lounge has a bare-brick, inglenook fireplace, and furnishing that includes large armchairs and an intricately carved coffee table; the dining room is

adorned with drawings depicting the pub through the ages. Outside are two attractive beer gardens and a covered smoking area. Regular events include quiz nights and steak nights.

RINGWOOD
CANDLESTICKS INN

MAP F (2)

- 136 Christchurch Road, Ringwood, BH24 3AP
- 01425 472587   www.hotelnewforest.co.uk
- SU150046   50.8414, -1.7873
- 1100-1430, 1830-2300 Tu-Su.

◖◗ S ✗ ⌒ 🐴 ♿ ⊞ ❀ ⌐ P 🚌

- One guest from Ringwood.

How much beer would it take to fill an Olympic-sized swimming pool? Around 4.4million pints.

The pretty Candlesticks is a former cottage, thatched and with a dormer peering through the roof of its lower wing. Floral adornments enhance its appearance in summer. Two heavily-beamed rooms with open fireplaces accommodate diners, and beer from the adjacent Ringwood Brewery is served on gravity in the café bar. Accommodation is provided in a separate lodge. The pub is close to the Castleman Trailway, a path which follows part of the course of Castleman's Corkscrew, a disused railway line, and is carried across the Avon on its original bridges.

RINGWOOD
CROWN TAP

MAP F (3)

- 4 Southampton Road, Ringwood, BH24 1HY
- 01425 461027
- SU148052   50.8463, -1.7909
- 1100-2300 Mo-Sa; 1200-2230 Su.

❀ ⌐ 🚌

- Two guests.

If you collect beer bottles you're a labeorphilist.

The Georgian Crown Tap was formerly an autonomous appendage to the Crown Hotel (see Seven Fish); a broad, arched carriageway evinces its coaching past. It now revels in the status of a pure pub, unencumbered by the serving of meals or snacks. The walls of the bar and lounge area are adorned with old-style advertisements for detergents, comestibles and other goods. A separate room is home to a pool table and dart board, and there is outdoor seating to the rear of the pub.

RINGWOOD
ELM TREE

MAP F (4)

- ⌑ Hightown Road, Ringwood, BH24 3DY
- ☎ 01425 472516   www.elmtreeringwood.co.uk
- ↗ SU163048   50.8431, -1.7698
- ⏲ 1100-2300 Mo-Th; 1100-2400 Fr-Sa; 1200-2230 Su.

◖❙ S ✗ 🐕 🍴 ♿ ❀ ⊱ 🍲 P ⊟

- 🍺 Greene King: IPA, Old Speckled Hen, Abbot Ale; guests.

A very tasteful conversion of a thatched former farmhouse, with original beams (tall visitors beware!) and modern décor, the Elm Tree has a large, open-plan bar which is divided into several areas. Food is served all day at weekends and during summer. Regular events include Tuesday's spice night, Friday's lunchtime cod specials, two-for-one deals on Wednesday evening (pies) and Thursday evening (steaks), and live music on summer Sunday lunchtimes. The 'Barn Bar' function room has a skittle alley. In nearby Crow Lane is Liberty's Owl, Raptor and Reptile Centre.

RINGWOOD
FINNS

MAP F (5)

- ⌑ 25 Market Street, Ringwood, BH24 1AN
- ☎ 01425 474253   www.finnsatringwood.co.uk
- ↗ SU145052   50.8469, -1.7948
- ⏲ 1100-2300 Th; 1100-2400 Fr-Sa; 1100-2300 Su.

◖❙ S 🐕 ❀ 🍲 P ⊟

- 🍺 One beer from Ringwood; one guest.
- 🍎 Thatchers: Cheddar Valley; Westons: Vintage Organic.

A popular community pub with a long-serving landlord. Home-made food is available all day, and the pub is at its busiest at lunchtime and in the early evening. There are Wednesday folk evenings and other occasional music events featuring local talent. Occasional beer festivals add to the attraction. There are wheelchair ramps but narrow doors impose a restriction on size. The pub stands opposite the parish church of St Peter and St Paul.

RINGWOOD
FISH INN

The Bridges, West Street, Ringwood, BH24 2AA
01425 473185   www.thefishinn.net
SU142051   50.8460, -1.7991
1100-2300 Mo-Th; 1100-2400 Fr-Sa; 1200-2300 Su.

Ringwood: Best Bitter, Fortyniner; two guests.

This Tudor thatched building, with a large, riverside beer garden, stands below the westbound carriageway of the A31; easiest access from the town centre is via Market Place. Its many rooms, served from a single bar, are decorated in a calm and restrained style, and have a mixture of carpeted, boarded and tiled floors. Warmth from a wood-burning stove may be enjoyed from the comfort of a chesterfield. Food is available all day at weekends, and dishes will be adjusted on request to suit the needs of the gluten-intolerant.

RINGWOOD
INN ON THE FURLONG

12 Meeting House Lane, Ringwood, BH24 1EY
01425 475139   www.ringwoodbrewery.co.uk/pubs/puddetails.aspx?pid=8
SU147052   50.8469, -1.7924
1030-2300 Mo-Th; 1030-2400 Fr-Sa; 1100-2300 Su.

Jennings: Cocker Hoop; Ringwood: Best Bitter, Fortyniner, Old Thumper, seasonals; occasional guests.

A large pub whose interior is divided into several areas. Its proximity to the town centre makes it popular with shoppers, and it is often the first stop for the discerning drinker alighting at the nearby bus stands. Food is available all day, and on Wednesdays a specials night is run in association with a local Indian restaurant. Children are allowed in the conservatory or family room; dogs are not permitted in dining areas.
Wall-mounted televisions show (usually silent) sport, and there is live music on Tuesday and Saturday.

RINGWOOD
LAMB INN

MAP F (8)

2 Hightown Road, Ringwood, BH24 1NW
01425 473721   www.lambinnringwood.co.uk
SU150048   50.8426, -1.7872
1200-2300 Mo-We; 1200-2400 Th-Sa; 1200-2230 Su.

Ringwood: Best Bitter.

A large, Victorian pub, seemingly composed of a number of different buildings, with slate roofs, dormers and heavy labels. The bar is large, L-shaped and open-plan; it has an area dedicated to the pleasures of pool and darts, and two televisions which show sport, enthusiasm for which is reflected in the pub's sponsoring of a football team and three cricket teams. Marty's Pizzas operates from an open-plan kitchen in the pub; pizzas are served from 5pm until 10pm daily, except bank holidays.

RINGWOOD
ORIGINAL WHITE HART

MAP F (10)

Market Place, Ringwood, BH24 1AW
01425 472702   www.originalwhitehartpub.co.uk
SU146052   50.8467, -1.7939
1030-2300 Mo-Sa; 1100-2230 Su.

Ringwood: Best Bitter, guests.

This very handsome building dates back to before the 18th century. The legend of the original White Hart, named by Henry VII following his capture of such a beast, may be an allegory of the War of the Roses. A nogged Victorian gable rises above the carriageway, and a pedimented entrance leads to two bars, beamed and with stained glass interior windows. The hotel has 15 bedrooms and a function room. Food is served all day, and there is a different theme or promotion every weekday evening.

RINGWOOD
RINGWOOD BREWERY

MAP F (11)

✉ 138 Christchurch Road, Ringwood, BH24 3AP
☏ 01425 470303   www.ringwoodbrewery.co.uk
↗ SU150046   50.8411, -1.7870
🕐 0930-1700 Mo-Sa.

🍺 Ringwood: Best Bitter, Boondoggle, Fortyniner, Old Thumper, seasonals.

The vanguard of the micro-brewery revolution was founded in 1978. It outgrew its original site, and in 1986 moved to its present location, that of the long-deceased Tunks Brewery. In 2007 Ringwood was sold to Marston's, in whose hands production continues to increase. The shop sells Ringwood beers in casks, from casks and in bottles, a selection of bottled beers from other Marston's breweries, merchandise, and beery comestibles. Brewery tours (booking essential, no children under eight) take place on Saturday afternoons and on summer Sunday afternoons. Groups may book evening tours.

RINGWOOD
SEVEN FISH

MAP F (12)

✉ 8 Southampton Road, Ringwood, BH24 1HY
☏ 01425 480472   www.sevenfish.co.uk
↗ SU148052   50.8461, -1.7910
🕐 1000-2300.

🍺 None

An ancient clay tablet discussing the preparation of beer is the oldest document known to man.

The Seven Fish occupies part of the former Crown Hotel, a handsome, 18th century, tile-hung building. The adjacent Crown Tap (see separate entry) was once part of the hotel. This bright and airy restaurant and bar, furnished in modern style, specializes in fish, but its menu is wide-ranging enough to satisfy carnivore and vegetarian. It opens for breakfast, and proceeds to the service of lunch, afternoon tea, dinner and cocktails. There are occasional live music, food and wine tasting events.

RINGWOOD
STAR INN

MAP F (13)

⌨ 12 Market Street, Ringwood, BH24 1AW
☎ 01425 473105   www.thestarringwood.co.uk
↗ SU145052   50.8468, -1.7943
🕐 1100-2300 Mo-Sa; 1200-2230 Su.

🍺 Brains: SA; Hop Back: Summer Lightning; Ringwood: Best Bitter; guests.
🍏 Moles: Black Rat.

This 17th century building was originally the Star Brewery. It is now a two bar local, with a log fire and some original beams. Food from the wide-ranging menu is available until 9pm, and includes Thai specialities and seasonal seafood. Events include a quiz night on Tuesday and a meat draw on Sunday. The principal function of the rear bar's television is to show rugby matches.

Accommodation is available in eight en-suite rooms. There is ramp access to the rear bar but no disabled toilet facility.

ROCKBOURNE
ROSE & THISTLE

MAP A (8)

Rockbourne, SP6 3NL
01725 51823   www.roseandthistle.co.uk
SU113183   50.9648, -1.8404
1100-1500, 1800-2300 Mo-Fr; 1100-2300 Sa; 1200-2000 (2230 summer) Su.

◖◗ S ⅋ ⑂ ☃ ✿ ⌇ ⚒ P

Fuller's: London Pride; Palmers: Copper Ale; Timothy Taylor: Landlord; one guest in summer and occasionally in winter.

One guest.

Situated in a pretty village with Roman villa and part-Norman church, this picturesque, thatched building rose in the 16th century as three cottages, and served as a bakery before becoming a pub in the 1890s. Saved from closure in the 1990s by a local consortium, but later sold to a private owner, it still bears the name of Strong's (brewery, long closed) of Romsey. The cosy restaurant / lounge and flagstone-floored bar have handsome fireplaces, and seating includes settles. Food (not Sunday evening) includes local beef, pork and game, and home-made puddings; booking is advisable.

ON BARRELS AND CASKS

You will hear of pubs where beer is served 'straight from the barrel' – there are no such pubs! There are some, however, where it is served from the cask. In the brewing industry, the word barrel is not the generic term for a container, it refers only to one specific, rather large, size – 36 gallons. For a real ale container the proper term is a cask and for processed beer it is a keg.

Casks come in many sizes, traditionally sub-divisions of the 36 gallon barrel although recently some metric sizes have also appeared; each size has its own name.

PIN – 4½ gallons, rarely seen now for economic reasons.

FIRKIN – 9 gallons, almost the de facto standard these days, small enough to be manhandled by one (muscular) person.

KILDERKIN – 18 gallons, the size of choice for many licensees for their most popular beers,

BARREL – 36 gallons, rarely seen as a cask but still always used when describing a brewery's production – a '10 barrel brewery' can produce 360 gallons at each brew.

HOGSHEAD – 54 gallons, these monsters are now just history; a full wooden one would weigh a third of a ton.

SOPLEY

AVON
NEW QUEEN

MAP O (3)

Ringwood Road, Avon, BH23 7BG
01425 672432   www.thenewqueen.co.uk
SZ146986   50.7873, -1.7934
1100-2300 Mo-Sa; 1200-2230 Su.

Hall & Woodhouse: Badger First Gold, Tanglefoot, seasonals.

The pub was built in the 1800s and named in honour of Queen Victoria; subsequent extensions have doubled its size. Inside there are oak beams, wooden floors, bare-brick walls, open fires and standard lamps. Sturdy wooden tables and chairs are well spaced around the large room, which also has a number of small side areas ideal for quiet dining and drinking. The extensive menu includes Sunday roasts. Outside is a riverside beer garden with decking and a large children's play area.

AVON
TYRRELL'S FORD

MAP F (14)

Ringwood Road, Avon, BH23 7BH
01425 672646   www.tyrrellsford.co.uk
SZ148996   50.7961, -1.7910
1100-2300 Mo-Sa; 1200-2230 Su.

Flack Manor: Double Drop; Ringwood: Best Bitter; guests.

This 18th century building, set in eight acres of grounds, is 100 yards from the Avon Valley Path. Originally the residence of Lord and Lady Manners, it derives its name from that of William Rufus's killer, who during his flight had his horse's shoes reversed at a nearby smithy. The comfortably-furnished lounge has an open fire, a mural, and a staircase which opens into a minstrels' gallery. The bar looks out onto the garden, and there is an elegant, wood-panelled dining room. The varied menu ranges from snacks to full meals.

SOPLEY
SOPLEY MILL

MAP O (4)

Mill Lane, Sopley, BH23 7AU

01425 674196   www.sopleymill.com

SZ156966   50.7696, -1.7798

1100-2300 Tu-Sa; 1100-1800 Su; additional opening on bank holidays.

Wells and Young's: Courage Best.

The beautifully-situated Riverside Sopley Mill Bar & Restaurants sits astride a millstream off the River Avon, in an area rich in wildlife. Milling ceased in 1955 but some well-preserved machinery survives. The ground floor Swannery Restaurant is beamed and overlooks the riverside lawn. The top two floors, reserved for special occasions, contain a function suite and the Riverview Restaurant. The riverside garden and front patio are available all year for alfresco dining. Morning coffee and afternoon tea are served, and Ringwood ales are available by the bottle.

SOPLEY
WOOLPACK INN

MAP O (6)

Ringwood Road, Sopley, BH23 7AX

01425 672252   www.woolpackinnsopley.co.uk

SZ156968   50.7713, -1.7790

1100-2300 Mo-Sa; 1200-2230 Su.

Ringwood: Best Bitter, Fortyniner; Wadworth: 6X.

The Woolpack was built in the mid-19th century, and was a favourite haunt of those stationed at RAF Sopley, a nearby radar station closed in 1974. This lovely, thatched pub lies between the Ringwood – Christchurch road and a spur of the river Avon. There are two bars, both low-beamed (take care!), carpeted and with exposed brickwork, and a large conservatory. The riverside garden is reached via a little footbridge. Food is served all day at weekends. Monday night is quiz night.

MOUNT PLEASANT
PASSFORD HOUSE HOTEL

MAP L (7)

⌖ Mount Pleasant Lane, Mount Pleasant, SO41 8LS
☎ 01590 682398   www.passfordhousehotel.co.uk
↗ SZ300977   50.7773, -1.5747
🕐 1100-2300.

◖▶ S ✗ ⛷ 🐂 ♿ 🛏 ❀ ⛺ P

🍺 None

A large, country house hotel set in extensive, wooded grounds. The many facilities include putting green, tennis courts, croquet lawn, leisure complex and swimming pool, and there are riding stables nearby. Both bar and restaurant are open to non-residents; the restaurant is closed on Monday lunchtimes. The bar area has comfortable seats and is decorated with antique pictures. It offers pub-style cooked food when the restaurant is open, and sandwiches at other times. There is also a lounge area with comfortable sofas, and seating outside on the front lawn.

SWAY
HARE & HOUNDS

MAP L (5)

⌖ Durnstown, Sway, SO41 6AL
☎ 01590 682404   www.pubsnewforest.co.uk/?page_id=3
↗ SZ283986   50.7871, -1.5997
🕐 1100-2300.

◖▶ S ✗ ⛷ 🐂 ❀ ↳ ⛺ P 🚌 🛏

🍺 Ringwood: Best Bitter; Timothy Taylor: Landlord; one guest.

This long, narrow pub, built over 200 years ago as a coaching inn, stands at the edge of a heath. The beamed, farmhouse-style interior is divided into several separate seating areas. At the rear is a long, narrow, sheltered garden with a children's play area. Food is served all day; occasional themed evenings

include Indian and Mexican. Sunday night is quiz night, and the pub runs a golfing society. 1¼ miles south is Sway Tower, 218 feet of unreinforced concrete built around 1879 by a retired Indian judge.

SWAY
SWAY MANOR HOTEL

MAP L (12)

📧 Station Road, Sway, SO41 6BA
☎ 01590 682754   www.swaymanor.com
↗ SZ277983   50.7839, -1.6078
🕐 1000-2300.

◖▮ S ✕ ⛲ 🐎 ♿ 🛏 ❀ ⚑ P ⇌ 🚌

🍺 Ringwood: Best Bitter.

"Dost thou think, because thou art virtuous, there shall be no more cakes and ale?"
WILLIAM SHAKESPEARE
1564–1616

Built as a house in 1906, requisitioned by the military during World War II, renovated and opened as the White Rose Hotel in 1968, and given its current name following sale in 2002. The Sway Manor is a handsome, brick-built edifice with a fine entrance and a pretty belvedere. Its conservatory restaurant (one of three dining rooms) overlooks five acres of attractively laid out garden, and features local produce (some as local as the herb garden) in its essentially English menu. Music and other events are hosted throughout the year. Opposite is the ArtSway art gallery.

Bucklers Hard and the Beaulieu River (Beaulieu)

TOTTON AND ELING

CALMORE
SAXON INN

- Calmore Drive, Calmore, SO40 2SH
- 023 8086 0297
- SU341145   50.9291, -1.5157
- 1130-2300 Mo-Th; 1100-2400 Fr-Sa; 1200-2230 Su.

◖❱ S 🐕 🐎 ⛏ ♿ P 🚌

- Ringwood: Best Bitter.

A modern pub whose interior has a traditional feel, the Saxon stands in a housing estate to the northwest of Totton. It has a spacious lounge, and a public bar with pool table, two dart boards and televised sport. On the lawned area outside are picnic tables. Food, which is served all day, includes roast dinners on Wednesday and Sunday, and a takeaway curry service is offered. Events include Sunday's quiz night and meat draw, and monthly live music, karaoke or disco.

ELING
ANCHOR INN

- Eling Lane, Eling, SO40 9GD
- 023 8066 3323   www.theanchorinneling.co.uk
- SU365126   50.9119, -1.4814
- 1100-2300 Mo-Sa; 1200-2230 Su.

◖❱ S ✗ 🐕 🐎 ⛏ ♿ 🦀 🍴 🎿 P 🚲 🚌

- Ringwood: Best Bitter, Fortyniner; one guest.

This 200 year old building stands beside Eling Creek. It offers views of moored yachts and, beyond stacks of shipping containers, Southampton's docks. It is within yards of one of the UK's two remaining working tide mills. The interior is woody, with comfortable seating that includes leather armchairs. There is a separate dining room, and outside are a patio and a covered smoking area. Events include regular quiz nights and summer weekend music. Also in summer a tack and tackle stall provides children with the wherewithal to fish for crabs.

ELING
KING RUFUS

MAP E (7)

  Eling Hill, Eling, SO40 9HE
023 8086 8899   www.thekingrufus.co.uk
SU367121   50.9074, -1.4783
1100-1500, 1800-2300 Mo-Sa; 1100-2230 Su.

Ringwood: Best Bitter; three guests.

The King Rufus was built in the 1850s; pictures and memorabilia from the Victorian era adorn the walls. A flagstone floor leads to an L-shaped bar with an open fire and an upright piano. To the rear is a dining area with access to the gravelled garden, which has a children's play area and a pétanque terrain. The menu includes several vegetarian options; Sunday's food service is from midday until 4pm. There are monthly country-themed food nights, a beer festival in June, and occasional quizzes and live music.

ELING
VILLAGE BELLS

MAP E (18)

  Eling Hill, Eling, SO40 9HE
023 8066 0837   www.thevillagebells.weebly.com
SU367121   50.9073, -1.4781
1200-1500, 1700-2300 Mo-Fr; 1200-2400 Sa; 1200-2230 Su.

Ringwood: Best Bitter, Fortyniner; three guests.

The pub was built around 1800. Its interior is a single space whose main part has a wooden floor, wooden beams, television, and an open fire; to one side is a carpeted area with comfortable sofas. Sunday's food service is from midday until 4pm; no food is served on Monday evenings. Wednesday is quiz night, and there is occasional live music. Nearby St Mary's church, the parish church of Totton, was much-restored in the 19th century; its interior remains essentially medieval, and is worth a visit.

HOUNSDOWN
NEW INN   MAP E (8)

⌨ Main Road, Hounsdown, SO40 7EP
☎ 023 8066 0480
↗ SU354120   50.9070, -1.4971
🕐 1700-2330 Mo-Th; 1200-2400 Fr-Sa; 1200-2230 Su.
🦮 🏨 ♿ ❀ 🍺 P 🚌

🍺 Ringwood: Best Bitter.

This two bar pub, formerly the Red Deer, is situated on a service road alongside and below the A35. One bar has a pool table (free play on Tuesdays), dartboard and televised sport; the other has comfortable chairs and a bar billiards table, and is sometimes used for private functions. This community pub holds regular events, and is home to darts, pool and two football teams. Although no food is served, menus for local takeaways are available at the bar. Children are welcome until 9pm.

TOTTON
ELEPHANT AND CASTLE   MAP E (4)

⌨ 40 Commercial Road, Totton, SO40 3AG
☎ 023 8087 2128
↗ SU361133   50.9188, -1.4872
🕐 1000-2300 Mo-Th; 1000-2400 Fr-Sa; 1200-2300 Su.
◖ S 🦮 🏨 ❀ 🍺 🏧 P 🚲 🚌

🍺 Ringwood: Best Bitter.

The Elephant and Castle is one of the oldest pubs in Totton, and has an odd-looking single-storey wing to the front, with pitched and flat roof. The pub has two rooms, both smartly decorated: the low-ceilinged public bar has a games area at the rear, with a pool table and dartboard; the lounge is comfortable and has its own little bar. Outside, beyond the lounge, is a covered area for drinkers and smokers. There is live music at weekends.

TOTTON
KEYS

⌨ 18 Commercial Road, Totton, SO40 3BY
☏ 023 8086 2154
↗ SU360133   50.9187, -1.4883
⏱ 1000-2300 Mo-Th; 1000-2400 Fr-Sa; 1200-2300 Su.

🍺 Two guests.

One of the more attractive buildings in central Totton, the former Cross Keys was built in the late 18th century. It has three storeys, a hipped roof, dentilled eaves and a mixture of segment and straight headed windows. Entry from the street is into a space akin to a hotel reception area; beyond this and higher is a nicely-furnished and well-lit bar, and another large seating area. Pool and darts are played. Food is served until 6pm every day.

TOTTON
OLD FARMHOUSE

⌨ Ringwood Road, Totton, SO40 8EA
☏ 023 8086 2399
↗ SU350132   50.9174, -1.5026
⏱ 1100-2300 Su-Th; 1100-2400 Fr-Sa.

🍺 Greene King: IPA; one guest.

Part of the pub was indeed formerly a farmhouse. It is a large building built of brick in Flemish bond, and with a deep roof from which protrude dormers; a single-storey extension is sympathetic but unflattering. One end of the large, L-shaped bar has chest-high tables, tall stools, and a dartboard; the other opens out into a large seating area with several alcoves. The Old Farmhouse is a Hungry Horse, serving food from opening time until not long before closing. There is sports television and monthly live music.

TOTTON
PEG & PARROT

- ▭ 44 Rumbridge Street, Totton, SO40 9DS
- ☽ 023 8086 4614
- ↗ SU361129   50.9151, -1.4872
- ⏱ 1100-2300 Mo-We; 1100-2400 Th-Sa; 1100-2300 Su.

    ♿ ✿ ⌐ ⛺ ⇌ 🚌

- 🍺 Three guests.

The external appearance of this pub still suggests its previous life as a shop; it was formerly a draper's, and before that a greengrocer's. Within is a delightfully old-fashioned and cosy room with an L-shaped bar; its beamed ceiling is festooned with old cider jars; its walls are adorned with old pictures, some dating from the early 1900s. Many regulars are horse-racing enthusiasts, and horse-racing is the principal output of the television. Outside there is a covered smoking area.

TOTTON
PLAYERS

- ▭ Water Lane, Totton, SO40 3GX
- ☽ 023 8086 0330
- ↗ SU350136   50.9214, -1.5032
- ⏱ 1100-2300 Mo-Th; 1100-2400 Fr-Sa; 1200-2230 Su.

    S ⛷ 🎯 ✿ ⌐ ⛺ P 🚌

- 🍺 Ringwood: Old Thumper.

"Life ain't all beer and skittles, and more's the pity; but what's the odds, so long as you're happy?"
GEORGE DU MAURIER
1834–1894

Players stands a short distance from Totton College. The pub was built as the Cooper's Arms in the 1930s, and was given its current name some 50 years later. The public space consists of a lounge area and a games area, with a real fire in each; one long bar stretches between the two via a third, small, seating area. Food consists of snacks such as pies and sandwiches. There is televised sport and twice-monthly live music.

TOTTON
SALMON LEAP

MAP E (14)

⌨ Testwood Lane, Totton, SO40 3BR
☎ 023 8086 2694
↗ SU361140   50.9243, -1.4878
🕐 1200-1500, 1630-2300 Mo-We; 1200-2400 Th-Sa; 1130-2300 Su.

🍺 Flack Manor: Double Drop or Ringwood: Best Bitter.

This post-war pub has a two storey centre, either side of which is a single-storey wing. The façade presents an extraordinary amount of glazing for a pub. There are two bars: a public (with pool table and dartboard) and lounge. Each bar is entered through its own door in one of the wings. There is live music on the last Friday of the month. The pub stands at the edge of the marshes of the Lower Test Nature Reserve, close to the Test Way and a salmon leap.

TOTTON
SWAN INN

MAP E (16)

⌨ 4 High Street, Totton, SO40 9HN
☎ 023 8086 2185
↗ SU363131   50.9162, -1.4845
🕐 1200-2300 Mo-Th; 1200-2400 Fr-Sa; 1200-2230 Su.

🍺 Ringwood: Best Bitter.

This handsome set of buildings bears the date 1879 on a tile-hung gable above a brick-nogged first storey over a carriageway entrance. The public bar has a curved counter, a pool table and a dartboard. The wood panelled lounge, which is available for use as a function room, has a maritime theme, with portholes and nautical pictures on the walls. Food is not served at weekends. There is live music twice a month. Those seeking to comfort the inner child should visit the traditional sweet shop in nearby Eling Lane.

TOTTON AND ELING

TOTTON
TESTWOOD

MAP E (17)

⌖ Salisbury Road, Totton, SO40 3ND
☎ 023 8086 8210   www.gkpubs.co.uk/pubs-in-totton/testwood-pub
↗ SU349147   50.9309, -1.5041
🕐 1100-2300 Su-Th; 1100-2400 Fr-Sa.

◖▶ S ➘ ♿ ❀ ╚ P 🚌

🍺 Greene King: IPA; one guest.

This roadside pub, formerly the Testwood Hotel, has a conservatory along its front, before which is an entrance porch surmounted by a huge wooden gable; dormers cower behind. The large, single bar caters for both drinkers and diners, and serves home-cooked pub fare from midday to 9pm every day. The large, grassed garden has picnic benches, and a climbing frame for younger visitors. Poker is played on Tuesday nights. The Test Way passes nearby on its route across the marshes.

CANADA
ROCKINGHAM

- Canada Road, Canada, SO51 6DE
- 01794 322473   www.therockingham.co.uk
- SU289179   50.9603, -1.5893
- 1800-2300 Mo; 1100-1500, 1800-2300 Tu-Sa; 1200-1500, 1800-2230 Su.

    ◖▷ S ✕ ☙ ♞ ♿ ❀ ⛺ P ▥

Flack Manor: Double Drop; one guest.

The Rockingham stands in the hamlet of Canada, named after the country by settlers with farming ambitions. It was built in the 19th century as a chapel, but never used for worship, and later served as a school and as an alcohol store. The principal bar has modern décor, and its furnishing includes sofas; the erstwhile rear bar is reserved for functions. There is outdoor seating in front of the building and a small, grassed area to the rear. The pub is popular with the Canada Common dog-walking fraternity.

WHITSBURY
CARTWHEEL

MAP A (3)

⌨ Whitsbury Road, Whitsbury, SP6 3PZ
☎ 01725 518362   www.cartwheeling.co.uk
↗ SU128188   50.9690, -1.8184
🕐 1130-1430, 1800-2300 Mo-Fr; 1130-2300 Sa; 1200-2230 Su.

◖▶ S ⟁ ♞ ♿ ❀ ⌐ ⚒ P

🍺 Ringwood: Best Bitter, Fortyniner, one seasonal.

Whitsbury hides among the hills of borderland, where Hampshire rolls towards Dorset and Wiltshire. It is racehorse country; *Desert Orchid* was trained at Whitsbury Manor Stables. This 18th Century building was originally farm cottages, and has housed a wheelwright's and the village bakery (a defunct oven remains). The interior is on two levels and divided into several areas – beamed, wood-panelled, bare-bricked, and with seating that includes settles and pews. Food is available all day Saturday, and there are beer festivals at Easter and during the last weekend in July.

Saxon St Mary's Church, Breamore (Breamore)

WOODGREEN
HORSE & GROOM

- Woodgreen, SP6 2AS
- 01725 510739   www.horseandgroom-newforest.co.uk
- SU170176   50.9577, -1.7585
- 1200-1500, 1800-2300 Mo-Fr; 1200-2300 Sa; 1200-2230 Su (winter).
  1100-1500, 1800-2300 Mo-Fr; 1100-2300 Sa-Su (summer).

Hall & Woodhouse: K & B Sussex, Badger First Gold, one seasonal.

This handsome pub in a small village on the edge of the National Park was originally two cottages. It has been sensitively extended, and within are numerous discrete, cosy and contrasting areas. Some tables are cask conversions, and benches remain attached to the walls of one of the brick porches. Food includes locally-sourced produce, and is served all day at weekends (not winter Sunday evenings). The Avon Valley Path is ¼ mile away.

MAPS KEY

Key to individual maps

Parish or guide boundary ..... ————

Pub location ...... ●

Parish name ...... *PARISH*

For Outline Map see inside back cover.

Based on Ordnance Survey OpenData™ files.
Contains Ordnance Survey data © Crown copyright and database right 2011.

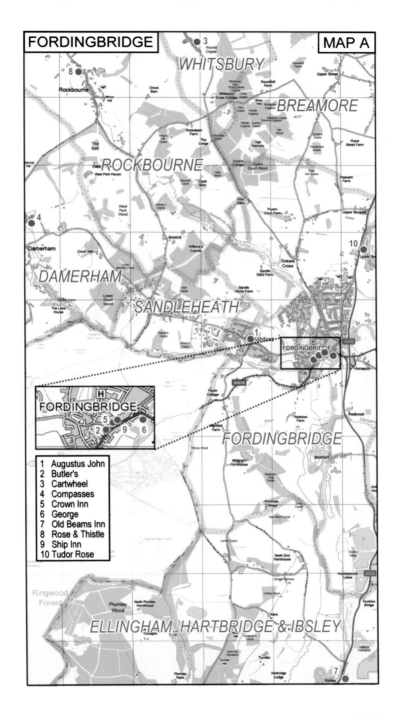

FORDINGBRIDGE

MAP A

WHITSBURY

BREAMORE

ROCKBOURNE

DAMERHAM

SANDLEHEATH

FORDINGBRIDGE

ELLINGHAM, HARTBRIDGE & IBSLEY

1 Augustus John
2 Butler's
3 Cartwheel
4 Compasses
5 Crown Inn
6 George
7 Old Beams Inn
8 Rose & Thistle
9 Ship Inn
10 Tudor Rose

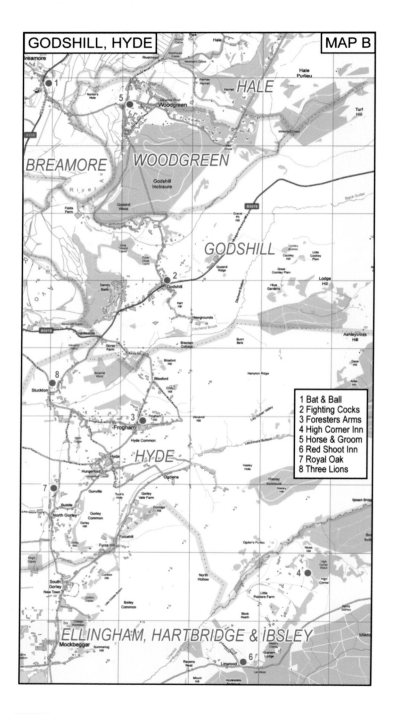

GODSHILL, HYDE

MAP B

1 Bat & Ball
2 Fighting Cocks
3 Foresters Arms
4 High Corner Inn
5 Horse & Groom
6 Red Shoot Inn
7 Royal Oak
8 Three Lions

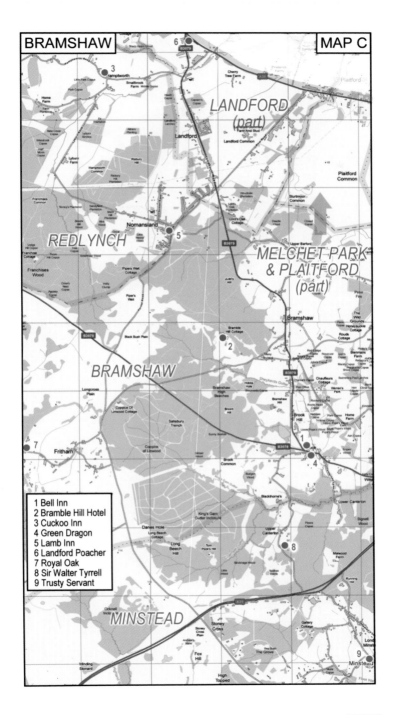

BRAMSHAW

MAP C

1 Bell Inn
2 Bramble Hill Hotel
3 Cuckoo Inn
4 Green Dragon
5 Lamb Inn
6 Landford Poacher
7 Royal Oak
8 Sir Walter Tyrrell
9 Trusty Servant

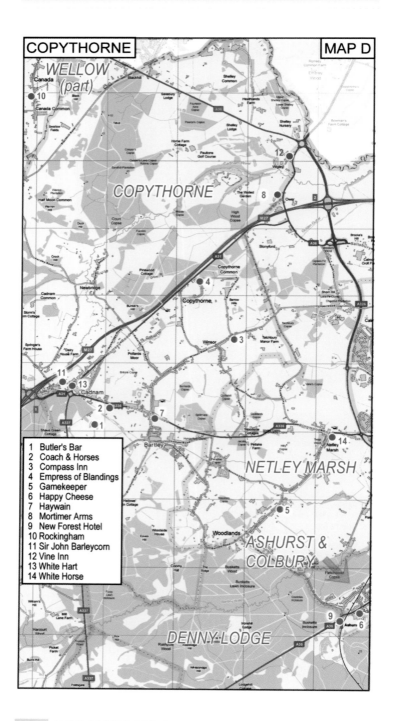

COPYTHORNE

MAP D

WELLOW (part)

COPYTHORNE

NETLEY MARSH

ASHURST & COLBURY

DENNY LODGE

1 Butler's Bar
2 Coach & Horses
3 Compass Inn
4 Empress of Blandings
5 Gamekeeper
6 Happy Cheese
7 Haywain
8 Mortimer Arms
9 New Forest Hotel
10 Rockingham
11 Sir John Barleycorn
12 Vine Inn
13 White Hart
14 White Horse

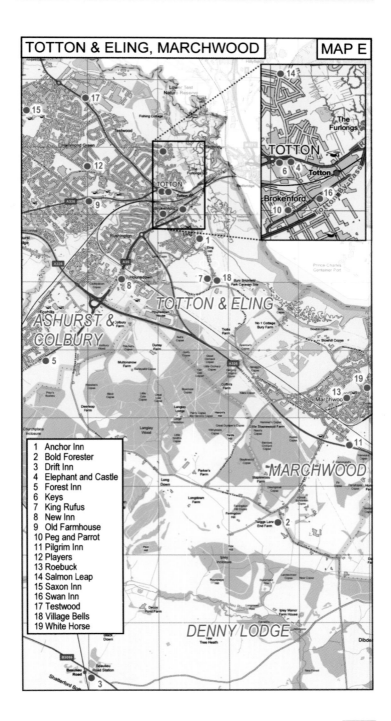

TOTTON & ELING, MARCHWOOD

MAP E

1 Anchor Inn
2 Bold Forester
3 Drift Inn
4 Elephant and Castle
5 Forest Inn
6 Keys
7 King Rufus
8 New Inn
9 Old Farmhouse
10 Peg and Parrot
11 Pilgrim Inn
12 Players
13 Roebuck
14 Salmon Leap
15 Saxon Inn
16 Swan Inn
17 Testwood
18 Village Bells
19 White Horse

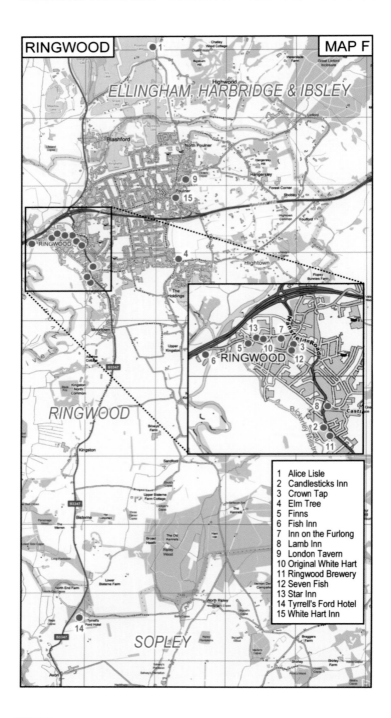

RINGWOOD

MAP F

ELLINGHAM, HARBRIDGE & IBSLEY

RINGWOOD

RINGWOOD

RINGWOOD

SOPLEY

1 Alice Lisle
2 Candlesticks Inn
3 Crown Tap
4 Elm Tree
5 Finns
6 Fish Inn
7 Inn on the Furlong
8 Lamb Inn
9 London Tavern
10 Original White Hart
11 Ringwood Brewery
12 Seven Fish
13 Star Inn
14 Tyrrell's Ford Hotel
15 White Hart Inn

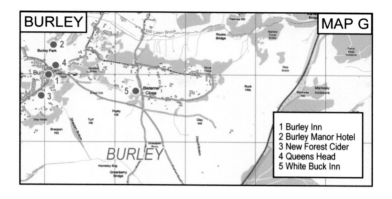

BURLEY

MAP G

1 Burley Inn
2 Burley Manor Hotel
3 New Forest Cider
4 Queens Head
5 White Buck Inn

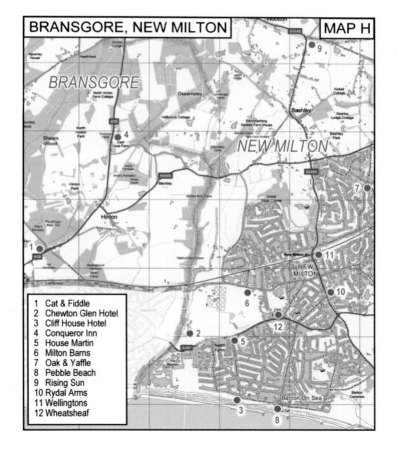

BRANSGORE, NEW MILTON

MAP H

1 Cat & Fiddle
2 Chewton Glen Hotel
3 Cliff House Hotel
4 Conqueror Inn
5 House Martin
6 Milton Barns
7 Oak & Yaffle
8 Pebble Beach
9 Rising Sun
10 Rydal Arms
11 Wellingtons
12 Wheatsheaf

BROCKENHURST, LYNDHURST

MAP I

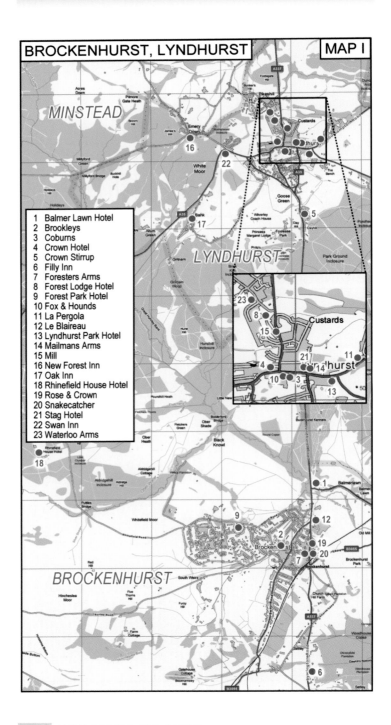

1   Balmer Lawn Hotel
2   Brookleys
3   Coburns
4   Crown Hotel
5   Crown Stirrup
6   Filly Inn
7   Foresters Arms
8   Forest Lodge Hotel
9   Forest Park Hotel
10 Fox & Hounds
11 La Pergola
12 Le Blaireau
13 Lyndhurst Park Hotel
14 Mailmans Arms
15 Mill
16 New Forest Inn
17 Oak Inn
18 Rhinefield House Hotel
19 Rose & Crown
20 Snakecatcher
21 Stag Hotel
22 Swan Inn
23 Waterloo Arms

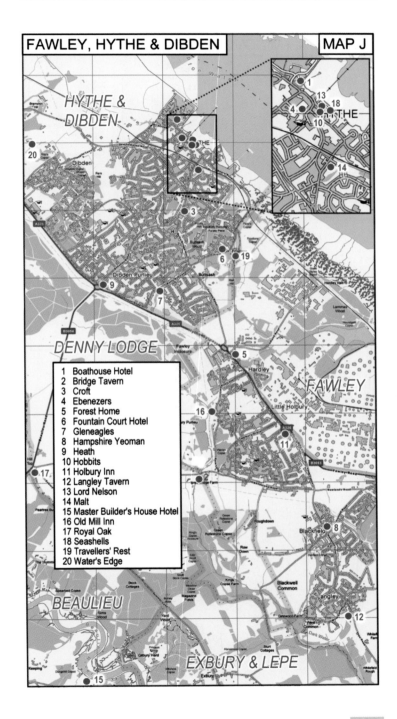

FAWLEY, HYTHE & DIBDEN

MAP J

1. Boathouse Hotel
2. Bridge Tavern
3. Croft
4. Ebenezers
5. Forest Home
6. Fountain Court Hotel
7. Gleneagles
8. Hampshire Yeoman
9. Heath
10. Hobbits
11. Holbury Inn
12. Langley Tavern
13. Lord Nelson
14. Malt
15. Master Builder's House Hotel
16. Old Mill Inn
17. Royal Oak
18. Seashells
19. Travellers' Rest
20. Water's Edge

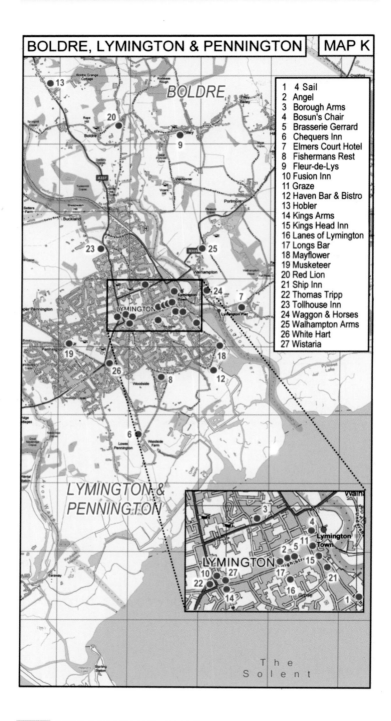

BOLDRE, LYMINGTON & PENNINGTON

MAP K

BOLDRE

LYMINGTON & PENNINGTON

LYMINGTON

1 4 Sail
2 Angel
3 Borough Arms
4 Bosun's Chair
5 Brasserie Gerrard
6 Chequers Inn
7 Elmers Court Hotel
8 Fishermans Rest
9 Fleur-de-Lys
10 Fusion Inn
11 Graze
12 Haven Bar & Bistro
13 Hobler
14 Kings Arms
15 Kings Head Inn
16 Lanes of Lymington
17 Longs Bar
18 Mayflower
19 Musketeer
20 Red Lion
21 Ship Inn
22 Thomas Tripp
23 Tollhouse Inn
24 Waggon & Horses
25 Walhampton Arms
26 White Hart
27 Wistaria

The Solent

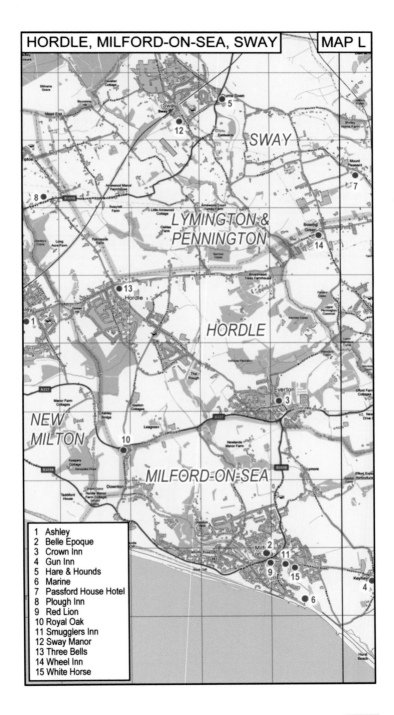

HORDLE, MILFORD-ON-SEA, SWAY

MAP L

1 Ashley
2 Belle Epoque
3 Crown Inn
4 Gun Inn
5 Hare & Hounds
6 Marine
7 Passford House Hotel
8 Plough Inn
9 Red Lion
10 Royal Oak
11 Smugglers Inn
12 Sway Manor
13 Three Bells
14 Wheel Inn
15 White Horse

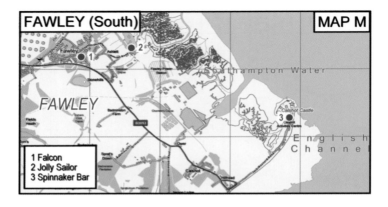

FAWLEY (South) — MAP M

1 Falcon
2 Jolly Sailor
3 Spinnaker Bar

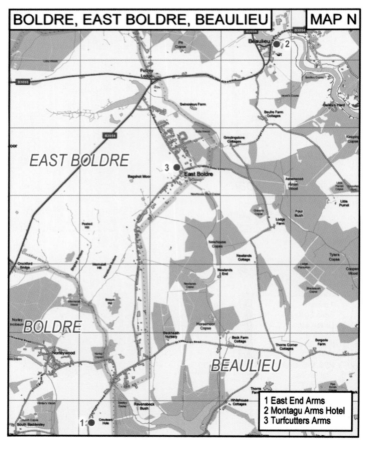

BOLDRE, EAST BOLDRE, BEAULIEU — MAP N

1 East End Arms
2 Montagu Arms Hotel
3 Turfcutters Arms

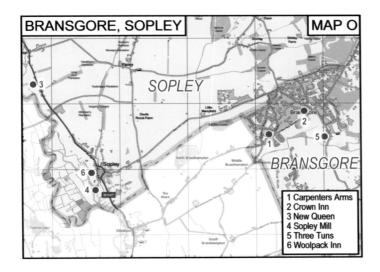

BRANSGORE, SOPLEY   **MAP O**

1 Carpenters Arms
2 Crown Inn
3 New Queen
4 Sopley Mill
5 Three Tuns
6 Woolpack Inn

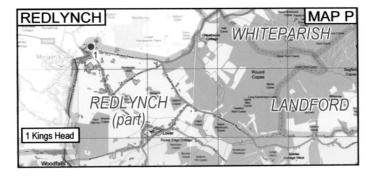

REDLYNCH   **MAP P**

1 Kings Head

CAMRA *INFORMATION*

HISTORY

By 1971 the United Kingdom's beer market was dominated by a sextet of brewers seemingly determined to flush quality and flavour from the nation's pubs. Their tiresome and heavily-promoted keg products were animated corpses; filtered and pasteurised liquids given a semblance of life by an excess of carbon dioxide.

Four friends determined that something must be done; they founded CAMRA, The Campaign for the Revitalisation of Ale. Preserving the acronym, the less tongue-twisting name, Campaign for Real Ale, was soon adopted. As a result the term Real Ale was born.

CAMRA has had many campaigning successes over the years, not least of which has been the revitalisation of ale. The United Kingdom has many hundreds of breweries producing quality beers in many styles, and quality beer is a global interest.

The job is not done; threats to the enjoyment of quality beer in quality pubs are ever present. CAMRA continues to champion drinkers' rights, and to promote and protect quality real ale and quality pubs.

SOUTHERN HAMPSHIRE BRANCH

The branch covers: Eastleigh, the New Forest, Southampton, and parts of the Test Valley and Winchester districts. It holds regular business and social meetings, runs beer festivals, and organizes visits to breweries and pubs further afield.

Visit our website at: www.shantscamra.org.uk

MEMBERSHIP

CAMRA has over 120,000 members, a diverse group brought together by love of good beer and belief in the continuing need for CAMRA's vigilance.

There is a membership form on the next page. Why not join us?

Benefits of membership include:
- a monthly newspaper and quarterly magazine;
- discounted entry to CAMRA beer festivals;
- discounted CAMRA publications;
- Wetherspoon real ale vouchers;
- the opportunity to support CAMRA's campaigns.

A Campaign of Two Halves

Fair deal on beer tax

Save Britain's Pubs!

Join CAMRA Today

Complete the Direct Debit form and you will receive 15 months membership for the price of 12 and a fantastic discount on your membership subscription.

Alternatively you can send a cheque payable to CAMRA Ltd with your completed form, visit www.camra.org.uk/joinus or call 01727 867201. All forms should be addressed to Membership Department, CAMRA, 230 Hatfield Road, St Albans, AL1 4LW.

Your Details

Title _____ Surname _____

Forename(s) _____

Date of Birth (dd/mm/yyyy) _____

Address _____

_____

_____ Postcode _____

Email address _____

Tel No(s) _____

Partner's Details (if Joint Membership)

Title _____ Surname _____

Forename(s) _____

Date of Birth (dd/mm/yyyy) _____

Direct Debit   Non DD

Single Membership   £20 ☐   £22 ☐
(UK & EU)

Joint Membership   £25 ☐   £27 ☐
(Partner at the same address)

For Young Member and concessionary rates please visit **www.camra.org.uk** or call **01727 867201**.

I wish to join the Campaign for Real Ale, and agree to abide by the Memorandum and Articles of Association

I enclose a cheque for _____

Signed _____ Date _____

Applications will be processed within 21 days

12/10

Campaigning for Pub Goers & Beer Drinkers

Enjoying Real Ale & Pubs

Join CAMRA today - www.camra.org.uk/joinus

Instruction to your Bank or Building Society to pay by Direct Debit

Please fill in the whole form using a ball point pen and send to:
Campaign for Real Ale Ltd. 230 Hatfield Road, St. Albans, Herts AL1 4LW

DIRECT Debit

Name and full postal address of your Bank or Building Society

To the Manager   Bank or Building Society

Address

Postcode

Name(s) of Account Holder

Branch Sort Code

☐☐ ☐☐ ☐☐

Bank or Building Society Account Number

☐☐☐☐☐☐☐☐

Reference

☐☐☐☐☐☐☐☐☐☐☐☐☐☐☐☐☐☐

Service User Number

| 9 | 2 | 6 | 1 | 2 | 9 |

FOR CAMRA OFFICIAL USE ONLY
This is not part of the instruction to your Bank or Building Society

Membership Number

Name

Postcode

Instructions to your Bank or Building Society
Please pay Campaign For Real Ale Limited Direct Debits from the account detailed on this instruction subject to the safeguards assured by the Direct Debit Guarantee. I understand that this instruction may remain with Campaign For Real Ale Limited and, if so will be passed electronically to my Bank/Building Society

Signature(s)

Date

Banks and Building Societies may not accept Direct Debit Instructions for some types of account.

DIRECT Debit

This Guarantee should be detached and retained by the payer.

The Direct Debit Guarantee

• This Guarantee is offered by all banks and building societies that accept instructions to pay by Direct Debits.

• If there are any changes to the amount, date or frequency of your Direct Debit The Campaign for Real Ale Ltd will notify you 10 working days in advance of your account being debited or as otherwise agreed. If you request The Campaign for Real Ale Ltd to collect a payment, confirmation of the amount and date will be given to you at the time of the request

• If an error is made in the payment of your Direct Debit by The Campaign for Real Ale Ltd or your bank or building society, you are entitled to a full and immediate refund of the amount paid from your bank or building society
 - If you receive a refund you are not entitled to, you must pay it back when The Campaign for Real Ale Ltd asks you to.

• You can cancel a Direct Debit at any time by simply contacting your bank or building society. Written confirmation may be required. Please also notify us.

NEW FOREST MARQUE

THE NEW FOREST MARQUE scheme is managed by the New Forest National Park Authority and New Forest District Council.

It exists to promote New Forest produce, and provide to the consumer an assurance of provenance and quality.

In assessing a product's eligibility, consideration is given to such matters as: where livestock was grazed, the source of cattle feed, and what percentage of a product's components is New Forest produce.

INDEX PUB NAMES

Pub name	Settlement	Map	Page
Empress of Blandings	Copythorne	D (4)	37
Falcon	Fawley	M (1)	48
Fighting Cocks	Godshill	B (2)	54
Filly Inn	Setley	I (6)	31
Finns	Ringwood	F (5)	101
Fish Inn	Ringwood	F (6)	102
Fisherman's Rest	Lymington	K (8)	69
Fleur-de-Lys	Pilley	K (9)	18
Forest Home	Hardley	J (5)	49
Forest Inn	Ashurst	E (5)	15
Forest Lodge Hotel	Lyndhurst	I (8)	80
Forest Park Hotel	Brockenhurst	I (9)	28
Foresters Arms	Brockenhurst	I (7)	28
Foresters Arms	Frogham	B (3)	57
Fountain Court Hotel	Hythe	J (6)	62
Fox & Hounds	Lyndhurst	I (10)	80
Fusion Inn	Lymington	K (10)	70
Gamekeeper	Woodlands	D (5)	90
George	Fordingbridge	A (6)	53
Gleneagles	Dibden Purlieu	J (7)	59
Graze	Lymington	K (11)	70
Green Dragon	Brook	C (4)	22
Gun Inn	Keyhaven	L (4)	86
Hampshire Yeoman	Blackfield	J (8)	47
Happy Cheese	Ashurst	D (6)	15
Hare & Hounds	Sway	L (5)	109
Haven Bar & Bistro	Lymington	K (12)	71
Haywain	Bartley	D (7)	35
Heath	Dibden Purlieu	J (9)	60
High Corner Inn	Linwood	B (4)	45
Hobbits	Hythe	J (10)	62
Hobler	Battramsley	K (13)	17
Holbury Inn	Holbury	J (11)	49
Horse & Groom	Woodgreen	B (5)	120
House Martin	Barton-on-Sea	H (5)	92
Inn on the Furlong	Ringwood	F (7)	102
Jolly Sailor	Fawley	M (2)	48
Keys	Totton	E (6)	114
King Rufus	Eling	E (7)	112
Kings Arms	Lymington	K (14)	71
Kings Head	Redlynch	P (1)	98
Kings Head Inn	Lymington	K (15)	72
La Pergola	Lyndhurst	I (11)	81
Lamb Inn	Nomansland	C (5)	97
Lamb Inn	Ringwood	F (8)	103
Landford Poacher	Landford	C (6)	65
Lanes of Lymington	Lymington	K (16)	72
Langley Tavern	Langley	J (12)	50

INDEX PUB NAMES

INDEX PUB NAMES

Pub name	Settlement	Map	Page
Salmon Leap	Totton	E (14)	116
Saxon Inn	Calmore	E (15)	111
Seashells	Hythe	J (18)	64
Seven Fish	Ringwood	F (12)	104
Ship Inn	Fordingbridge	A (9)	53
Ship Inn	Lymington	K (21)	74
Sir John Barleycorn	Cadnam	D (11)	36
Sir Walter Tyrrell	Canterton	C (8)	89
Smugglers Inn	Milford-on-Sea	L (11)	88
Snakecatcher	Brockenhurst	I (20)	30
Sopley Mill	Sopley	O (4)	108
Spinnaker Bar	Calshot	M (3)	47
Stag Hotel	Lyndhurst	I (21)	83
Star Inn	Ringwood	F (13)	105
Swan Inn	Emery Down	I (22)	78
Swan Inn	Totton	E (16)	116
Sway Manor Hotel	Sway	L (12)	110
Testwood	Totton	E (17)	117
Thomas Tripp	Lymington	K (22)	74
Three Bells	Hordle	L (13)	56
Three Lions	Stuckton	B (8)	58
Three Tuns	Bransgore	O (5)	24
Tollhouse Inn	Lymington	K (23)	75
Travellers Rest	Hythe	J (19)	64
Trusty Servant	Minstead	C (9)	89
Tudor Rose	Burgate	A (10)	51
Turfcutters Arms	East Boldre	N (3)	44
Tyrrell's Ford	Avon	F (14)	107
Village Bells	Eling	E (18)	112
Vine Inn	Ower	D (12)	38
Waggon & Horses	Walhampton	K (24)	19
Walhampton Arms	Walhampton	K (25)	20
Water's Edge	Dibden	J (20)	59
Waterloo Arms	Lyndhurst	I (23)	83
Wellingtons	New Milton	H (11)	95
Wheatsheaf	New Milton	H (12)	95
Wheel Inn	Bowling Green	L (14)	66
White Buck Inn	Burley	G (5)	34
White Hart	Cadnam	D (13)	37
White Hart	Pennington	K (26)	76
White Hart Inn	Poulner	F (15)	99
White Horse	Marchwood	E (19)	85
White Horse	Milford-on-Sea	L (15)	88
White Horse	Netley Marsh	D (14)	90
Wistaria	Lymington	K (27)	75
Woolpack Inn	Sopley	O (6)	108

INDEX SETTLEMENTS

INDEX *SETTLEMENTS*

INDEX *ACCOMMODATION*